The Boy of Hearts

Sirbrian Spease

Editing by Oliver Mills, Casper Cendre,
and Bread Tarleton

Illustrations by Rogue

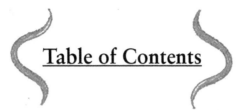

Table of Contents

Foreword

I first encountered Sirbrian Spease through listening
to his rendition of the popular Edwin Hawkins tune,
"Oh Happy Day," on YouTube. Even now, over a year
later, I remember Sirbrian's voice as bone-chillingly
beautiful and brimming with joy. I remember his
beaming face and the gap in his teeth, how his whole
body shook as he sang. The level of passion Sirbrian
put into that performance is equally evident in all of his
comics, stories, and letters to A.B.O. Comix over the
years. The time since Sirbrian first made contact with
our collective has been a long journey full of mutual
growth, admiration, and love.

One of his first letters came to us in August of
2017; it was a pitch for a longform comic called A
Homo Thug's Paradise. This comic, Sirbrian wrote,
would encapsulate the triumphs and challenges of
maintaining a relationship with his girlfriend Rico
while they both navigated the prison system. Sirbrian is
highly motivated by love, and all kinds of love at that.
As is evident throughout The Boy of Hearts, Sirbrian's
world revolves around his love for people like his older
brother Chris, his childhood friend Teka, his younger
foster brother Tyrone, and his imaginary lover Prince.
Each of these supportive relationships allows Sirbrian

to live within a different aspect of his identity, even when he must hide these parts of himself from the rest of the world.

Sirbrian is a person whose sense of self can survive all attacks, even those coming from within. Throughout both parts of his autobiographical novel, Sirbrian becomes acquainted with a dark alter ego named Devon--and Devon's unique capabilities. When Devon's mania, aggression, and paranoia are unleashed, all the rest of Sirbrian's being must take a backseat. Because Devon believes he knows how to act in Sirbrian's best interest, he often directs Sirbrian's actions towards his own violent goals.

Sirbrian frequently describes a process of surrendering his body over to Devon's near-superhuman strength and power. Sometimes this is done willingly, but more often Devon takes control of his and Sirbrian's shared body by force. When Devon is in control, nothing can stand in his way--not an abusive mother, not a pair of antagonistic boys at Sirbrian's foster home, not even Sirbrian himself. While a presence like Devon's sometimes protects Sirbrian from homophobic violence and other adversities, troubles arise when Devon intervenes with Sirbrian's ongoing psychotherapy.

At the other pole of Sirbrian's childhood personality is Donna, less an alter-ego and more an actualized form of himself instantiated by his older brother Chris. When Sirbrian decides to confide in Chris about the truth of his identity as 'a girl at heart,' Chris honors his sibling's bravery by calling Sirbrian his 'sister Donna.' While Sirbrian's identity has taken its own journey since childhood and since writing this book, the period of his life when Donna was allowed to take center stage remains incredibly poignant.

Donna is Devon's complement; where Devon is harsh and impulsive, Donna is soft and contemplative. Where Devon dominates, Donna thoughtfully considers others' opinions. And where Devon automatically dismisses everyone around him as homophobic--and, therefore, threatening--Donna enters every new relationship with an open mind and heart. Her relationship with Prince, Sirbrian's doll turned imaginary lover, is tender, hopeful, and surprisingly mature. Donna is steadfastly determined to find beauty in life, and to create it if it isn't obvious in her surroundings. When she reaches for crayons, she imagines them as eyeshadows and lipsticks perfect for decorating her face and showing the outside world just how beautiful she feels inside.

Donna exudes a level of comfort in her identity that is directly opposed to Devon's hypervigilance; taken together, their existence within a single person reminds us that we cannot enjoy self-confidence without also acknowledging fear--and we cannot always control which emotions influence our actions. Sirbrian's autobiography shows us that we are all made up of at least a little Devon, waiting behind our eyes to rush in and save our skin at any moment. We all contain some of Donna as well, within the most childlike and altruistic parts of ourselves.

In editing this story, I found myself relating to many of the experiences Sirbrian shares about his childhood. Emotions like anger at being misunderstood by one's peers, confusion at one's parents' self-destructive tendencies, and yearning for unconditional love resonated with me throughout the text. We may all relate to the experiences of finding friendship in unexpected places, moments where we had to grow up too fast, and times when our imagination was the best escape route from our circumstances. Sirbrian relates these experiences with clarity and candor, not to mention wry humor. Sirbrian's unique voice as a writer shone through for me in my first reading, and I hope that this is true for readers of this version as well.

The Boy of Hearts has undergone a substantial transformation from its first iteration. It began as a stack of handwritten pages, some written while Sirbrian was incarcerated and some since he has come home. As I transcribed the material, the story simply jumped off the page. From there, it was a matter of teasing out the individual voices of the characters--including the various parts of Sirbrian's personality--and watching as chapters emerged through the editing process. While the journey was largely smooth, there were some passages that were too painful to edit without time to process what I was reading. Sirbrian is such a powerful writer, and the occasional pain that comes from reading his work has less to do with the events he describes and more to do with the deftness with which he discusses his childhood trauma. I felt that I was at Sirbrian's side as he navigated his way through an abusive household and a rocky journey through the foster care system--all because of the brutally honest way he chose to tell his story. I have had trouble explaining the simple brilliance of this book to others, so I am overjoyed that it is now available for readers to experience it themselves.

I'm sure that my joy can't possibly compare to what Sirbrian is experiencing at having his story told in a way that allows so many people to access it. In some ways, this book is a commemoration of just how far Sirbrian has come in a mental health journey that began during his childhood. In the years since the end of The Boy of Hearts, Sirbrian has renewed his commitment to seeking comprehensive mental health treatment, over and over again. Even during his time in prison, he has stuck with therapy despite many people in his life giving up on him and deeming him a lost cause. Currently, he is working with a therapist on the outside who guides him through the times when his emotions become too painful to bear on his own. Overcoming trauma like what Sirbrian has experienced is a lifelong process, and telling the story of where he began is a single, crucial step.

I and the entire A.B.O. Comix team are grateful to know Sirbrian and to be a part of his life while he continues his journey to self-acceptance on the outside. We are grateful for his stories about how reading his comic submissions to A Queer Prisoner's Anthology to other queer and trans people in prison brought them together and created a mutually-supportive community. We are excited to continue to create an even larger community around Sirbrian's work; we hope he keeps creating, and we would be honored to remain a part of the process.

Oliver Mills

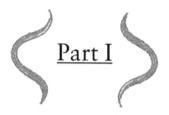

Part I

A gay boy's triumph, a maze of homophobia, and the darkness of a personality disorder.

Chapter 1

Double Dutch

Growing up in the hood is a challenge for any young boy. But growing up in the hood as a gay little boy in an abusive household is a struggle. I was misunderstood, a girl trapped inside the body of a boy. My mother, who was a pastor, could not accept me for who I was. On this journey, I will relive a childhood that I could only escape through my imagination. A handsome prince and a dominant alter ego would be my guides and guardians as I learned how to escape reality and learn to be me.

Not too many people can honestly say that they vividly remember being five years old. But for me, that age was the beginning of my journey. It was at that age that I came out and was proud to identify myself as gay. I still remember how red crayon felt and tasted on my big, chapped lips. When I really think about it, I'm reminded of the times I was abused. I was a victim of child abuse, and I'll never forget the pain that I had to endure.

I was a skinny Black kid from the projects, but I was determined to transition from a poor, nappy-headed boy into a princess even prettier than my mother. I didn't need Mom's help to make me pretty. I didn't even need her makeup. I had my imagination, which was as active and vivacious as any other kid's. Crayons could make me beautiful, so there was no need for makeup. I would stand on an old chair and look into the bathroom mirror.

I was proud of myself for how neatly my lips turned out, which gave me confidence to color my eyelids as well. I pretended that I had long, curly black hair like a princess in a fairytale. I would pretend to brush it every morning. I developed a routine to make sure I felt like a princess.

This make-believe world helped me to escape the harsh reality of growing up in the hood. In my imaginary world, everyone could see into my soul and accept me for the princess I was at heart. In that world, there was a prince named Prince. Prince was only an action figure, but he was my most prized possession. He loved me and accepted me for who I was. Each morning we would meet in the bathroom, our magical castle.

"Good morning, Prince! I love to see you smiling at me when I wake up," I would say.

"Good morning, my princess. It's good to know that I make you so happy," he'd reply.

"Oh, Prince, you are the only person that loves me for me."

"I feel the same way," he'd say. "As long as we have each other, you will never be alone."

"Am I beautiful?" I'd ask.

"You are gorgeous, my love. Your lips are like strawberries split in half." I'd feel myself blushing.

Prince then asked, "I wonder if they taste like strawberries. Do they?"

"Well, I don't know," I replied.

"Can I kiss them to see for myself, dear Princess?"

"Sure, Prince, go ahead. I see no reason why you shouldn't."

Prince then leaned in and kissed me. "Your lips really do taste like fresh strawberries! I wish I could eat them, for strawberries are my favorite fruit."

"If you ate them I'd never be able to kiss you again, silly!"

Prince then laughed as he said, "I almost forgot! My love, today we have a ball to attend!"

Overjoyed, I hurried to my mother's dirty clothes hamper. Prince sat on the sink, watching me as I dressed.

"You look beautiful, my princess. You will be the prettiest princess of all!" he said.

"Thank you, Prince," I replied. "This is why I love you so much." I lifted my prince figurine from the sink and we danced. As we danced, I imagined that other royalty watched us with envy. Suddenly, Mom's alarm clock went off. It was time to settle back into reality.

My mother was the pastor of the East Falls Tabernacle Church. She was a woman of faith and a strict mom. She couldn't possibly accept having a gay son, could she?

I had about five minutes to wash the makeup from my face and remove her clothes from my body. To the outside world, I was just a boy. A regular little boy who people assumed picked his nose and played with trucks. Boys played cops and robbers; they didn't play with dolls. But that was not me. I was a little girl at heart, scared that I would never be accepted for who I was. If my family would just accept me, everything else would be fine. It scared me to think how my mother would react, her being a strict Christian and all. And my brother, Chris: would he gay bash me and fail to protect me from other boys in the hood when they found out about my sexuality? People have been beaten and killed for coming out. I felt I had no choice but to keep it a secret, especially while living in the projects.

I recalled a time when I witnessed a transvestite get beaten to death. I was outside, playing on the bars with five other boys. They beat her repeatedly with sticks, taunting her until she expressed who she was. They threw rocks at her and hit her with a metal baseball bat. The more she cried out, pleading for her life, the more they assaulted her. Soon, the woman lay dead. No one ever came to her aid. This event was the talk of the hood for months and I believe that witnessing it was traumatic for me.

Our neighbors shared gossip all the time. The walls of our building were so thin that you could tell which program your neighbor was watching on TV. Any time my family would have an argument, gossip would spread throughout the projects. Because my mom was a pastor, people were quick to judge her and make assumptions about what kind of wife and mother she was. So when word began to spread about my father having an affair, it was juicy news to those who knew us. People must have held their ears to the wall the night my mother confronted him, because everyone was talking about it the next day. This holier-than-thou family maybe wasn't so holy after all.

Mom was too busy dealing with the problems of her church followers that she neglected the needs of her own family. This led my father into the arms of a teenage girl. Her name was Lisa; she was Dominican and had long black hair. Her hair and nails were always done, and my father would take her shopping.

The Boy of Hearts

One of my mom's friends told her that she had seen my father with a young woman fitting her description. Another woman saw them together as well. My mother's initial reaction was denial. Perhaps this woman was in need and Dad was doing the Christian thing by helping her. Unfortunately, this was not the case. A friend of the family confirmed that he was cheating after she witnessed them making out in Dad's car.

My mother eventually confronted my father about her friend's claims. One day, she burst into the apartment like a bull seeing red. Chris was playing video games in his room and I was playing with Prince. She was so angry, she didn't even notice I was wearing her dress.

"How dare you do this to me! How could you do this to your family? I've been so good to you," she cried.

"I'll tell you how!" Dad replied. "Church always comes before your family. Am I right, Gloria Spease?"

Mom began to weep as she explained, "I am a pastor. I'm obligated to serve the Lord in this way and you know that."

"You're obligated to do your duties as a wife! But you haven't, and that's why I'm doing this."

"God doesn't like adultery and doesn't like ugly," said Mom as she turned back toward the door, slamming it on her way out.

I didn't feel sorry for Mom. I smiled as I heard her making her way down the corridor, crying. Good, I thought, break Mom's heart.

I started to think about what Mom had recently said in a church lecture, about how homosexuality was an abomination in the eyes of God. She said that no matter what good people like me do on this earth, we will not make it into Heaven. Instead, we will descend to Hell and burn in the lake of fire. I prayed that Mom would never come back, and instead a new mother would be sent to me from God. This new mother would be one who I could open up to. Instead of being critical, she would be open-minded and accept me for the girl I was at heart.

One summer day, I was staring out from my window at the Black girls jumping double dutch. It made me sad that I couldn't be a part of it. When I was left home alone, I had started self-harming. I would punch myself in the head, bite myself, throw myself down the steps and more. I was abusing myself because I wanted to bring damage to the body that the Lord gave me. That way, if God saw me, He would ask me where the bruises and marks came from. Then, I would let Him know I had done it so He would know that there was a mix-up when He made me. I would tell Him: "I'm a girl in a boy's body. And, not to be disrespectful or anything, but could You please grant my wish and make me a girl?"

Sometimes in the past, Mom and Dad would confront me about the bruises. I'd lie and tell them I'd had a fight and that I was just sticking up for myself.

The Boy of Hearts

I'd get a quick lecture on how fighting doesn't solve anything and that would be the end of it.

In time, I started to realize that showing up bruised to my make-believe world made me look like the monster that Prince was supposed to save me from. Maybe I should stop coloring my face, I thought. I decided that I should bring this up to Prince. He was my love, my husband. Only his opinion mattered. So I let the bruises heal and then I called for Prince. I had my makeup on and wore a beautiful dress, looking prettier than ever for my one and only love. "Prince, my man and husband, I have something very important that I must talk to you about. It's very important and I hope and pray you won't be mad."

Prince responded, "My princess, my love. I am your prince, your love. Of all people, I should never judge you or be angry at you. We must not keep secrets. Tell me, what's wrong? Am I making you upset, my dear? If it's me, I'll fix it! Please, tell me!"

I spoke cautiously. "Well Prince, you should probably know that I have some bruises on my body--"

Prince shot back before I could even finish the sentence: "What! Who did this to you? Were you attacked by a monster? I can help you defeat it. Is it something I could have prevented?"

"No, Prince, there is no monster. And please don't ever think this is your fault! You're my prince, my love, the only person who loves me for me!"

Prince was concerned. "So why, my princess?" he asked. "Why did you do this to your body? Please tell me so that I can understand."

"Prince," I said, "I am a boy, I mean, a girl trapped inside of a boy's body. A girl that is trying to claw her way out of this body. I harmed myself to get God's attention. I want Him to fix the mistake He made."

"I see no mistakes, my love. God made you special, one of a kind," he reassured me.

"My prince, you can tell me the truth," I said, "I think my heart can handle it."

Again, Prince assured me his love was unconditional. "My princess, I fell in love with the person inside. I fell in love with your heart, whether it's the heart of a boy or a girl."

Then he asked: "My princess, does that heart love me?"

"Yes, my prince," I responded.

"Who owns that heart?" he asked.

"A little girl," I said.

"Then it's true, I am in love with a princess!"

Prince always knew how to make me feel better. "Thank you, Prince," I cried. "That's the sweetest thing anyone has ever said to me."

The Boy of Hearts

Prince asked, "My princess, does the world know of this special person that I am in love with?"

"No," I responded, "the only one who knows is you."

Then Prince said, "My princess, you don't mean anything to me if I can't share you with the world."

"What are you trying to say?" I asked, confused.

"Be the person who you're supposed to be. Why be someone you're not? There are creatures that are half human and half monster. Should they hide in the darkness because they appear different to the world?" Prince asked. What he said made a lot of sense.

"I've never thought of it that way, my prince," I said.

Prince continued, "Those creatures have some humans who respect them, who share their world with them. At the same time, there are humans who want them off the Earth. It is what it is.

"I love jumping rope," I interjected. "I mean, I love watching the girls jump rope. It looks so fun! I always wanted to be a part of that little world. So, are you saying I should step out into it and do what I want to do?" I asked.

"You are a princess trapped in a prince's body. There is nothing you can do about that," Prince replied. "What you can do is respect your heart by making it happy. Can you do that for me, my princess?"

"I will, my love!" I said confidently. "I will do everything I can to make this heart happy."

Prince asked, "How do I know that you will honor your promise?"

"Because everywhere I go, you will be in my pocket," I replied.

I took everything that Prince and I had talked about to heart. With each new day, Prince would be with me. I kept him in my pocket wherever I went.

One day, I asked my babysitter, Miss Tina, if I could go out to play. But Tina was lazy and mean and didn't want to be bothered with going all the way downstairs from our fourteenth-floor apartment. "Plus, it's too hot out," she said. "I ain't doing all that to watch your Black ass run around for an hour."

I blurted out, "You're just a lazy fat ass bitch!" as I ran into my room, slamming the door behind me. I thought for sure I would catch a whoopin' that day. As I sat in my room, I started to think about what I could do to get outside. Then, I got an idea.

My brother Chris, a stocky Black twelve-year-old, picked on me a lot. But when it came to other boys bullying me, he'd always have my back. My parents and Miss Tina both knew that Chris was protective of me; I could go out as long as I was with him. I thought about tactics I could use to get him away from his video games. I walked into his room and sat on the bed.

"Hey, Chris?" I said.

"What do you want? No, you cannot play video games with me," he replied.

"I got a way for you to make five dollars," I said, and then shrugged. "But I guess I'll leave you alone then, fool."

"I'm listening," he said. Mom gave us five dollars for allowance each. I thought that if I gave him my five dollars every week to watch me play, it would be a fair deal. I would miss that five bucks, but making my heart happy meant more to me than money. I explained to Chris that he had to take me outside and just watch me. Watch me and refrain from teasing me if I did anything weird. That was all.

"Shit, that's it?" he asked.

"Yes, and protect me from bullies," I added.

"That's my job as a big brother anyways, fool."

"Okay, then. It's a deal," I said. "But I want to go outside right now."

"There ain't even no boys outside right now," he said.

"I want to jump rope with the girls," I said, trying to sound as confident as I could.

"Really?" Chris asked. "Hey, that's kinda weird." He suddenly remembered his commitment and said, "Fine, let's go."

Down the steps I went, as fast as my little legs could move. Having Prince in my pocket gave me the courage to walk right up to the crowd of girls playing double dutch. The little girl in me was free! I wasn't sure how the girls would react to me asking to play. I hoped they would accept the real me, but they looked confused as I approached them.

"Can we help you?" one girl asked. "Look, if you're here to do that hit and run shit then trust and believe we gonna chase you down and fuck you up!" she yelled. Her name was Teka. She was a fat, dark-skinned girl, about three years older than me. I knew that the first thing I said, I had to make count. If I messed this up, I could ruin my chances of being accepted by the group of girls. But if I played my cards right, I could end up being best of friends with them.

I thought about what Prince had said. I knew his wisdom was there in this time of need. So I said it.

"Girl, everyday I watch you all double dutch. You all call that double dutch? I call that double or nothing!" I said sarcastically and puckered my lips while snapping my fingers.

The Boy of Hearts

"Ha, and you think you can do better? I have to see it to believe it," Teka said with an attitude as she started turning the rope. Right there, in that very moment, I felt as if the girls had accepted me. It wasn't the boy on the outside but the girl at heart that attracted them.

It was only a matter of time before I went from beginner to master at double dutch. It came quite naturally, since watching the girls for over a year made it easy to pick up. My inner female began to shine and the girls embraced it. I finally started to feel like I was becoming somebody and my self esteem was much better.

The boys in the project, however, weren't at all accepting. I was teased a lot, and sometimes they threw bricks and bottles at me. It became dangerous at points, when they tried to break my spirit by calling me a freak. I could have given in to the intimidation, but I didn't. I had made a promise to Prince and to myself, and I intended to keep it. I decided I was a girl at heart until the day I died and nobody had the power to take that from me. And let me tell you, the girls in the project would put their necks on the line for me. I truly had become one of them.

Chapter 2

Underwater

My brother Chris wasn't taking so well to my newfound identity. About two months later, Teka and I were returning from a Mr. Softy. She treated me to an ice cream cone and we discussed what we wanted to be when we grew up.

"Teka, what do you want to be when you're older?"

"Girl, I don't know. My mom has been teaching me about hair," she said, "so maybe a hairdresser. What do you think? Could I be a hairdresser, Sirbrian?"

"Yeah, I think so," I assured her. "If your mom keeps on teaching you until you know everything about hair, then why not?"

"Dang! You know what, Sirbrian? I've never thought of that. I bet it wouldn't even take that long at all to learn everything," she replied.

The Boy of Hearts

"Then Teka, you will be the youngest person in the world that does hair," I said, smiling wide.

"What do you want to be when you grow up?" she asked.

"What I want to be, I don't think the world will want," I replied.

"What's that?" she asked.

"I want to make clothes for people who are different like me. Clothes for boys who are really girls at heart and for girls who are boys at heart," I explained.

"Wow, that is different!" exclaimed Teka. "You'd be so famous if you did that!"

"Do you really think so?" I asked.

"Hell yeah!" she said, "You are a boy but you're a girl at heart. I know you ain't the only person God made who's like you." Teka had a point. I guessed she was referring to a man that lived on the fifth floor of the apartment building, wore makeup and women's clothes. I felt so comfortable in that moment that I shared a secret with Teka.

"Early in the morning, I put crayon on my face and dress up in my mom's clothes from the hamper. I pretend that the bathroom is a make-believe world where I am a princess who is married to a prince. Prince is really my toy," I said, ashamed, as I pulled Prince from my pocket to show her.

"Really?" she responded. "Sirbrian, you really do that every morning?"

"Yes," I admitted. "Right before I come out to play."

Our ice cream was melting under the hot summer sun as we hurried to eat it. Suddenly, I noticed my brother charging towards me. He looked angry and was literally pushing people out of his way to get to me. He was breathing heavily and I noticed his knuckles were bleeding. He reached us and slapped the ice cream cone out of my hand and onto the ground.

"Yo," he yelled, "You're taking this shit way too far! I'm done, do you hear me?! No more protection from me. I fight for you every day, and today I fought Tyrone!"

"Why would you fight Tyrone?" I asked. "He's your best friend."

"Well, he ain't no more," Chris replied. "I had to check his ass for running his mouth!"

I was confused. "What was he running his mouth about?"

"He said I'm going to turn into a faggot like you because we're brothers."

"What's a faggot?" I asked, already halfway to knowing the answer.

"You know what a faggot is, Sirbrian. A boy who likes other boys!" he exclaimed.

Chris was shouting so loudly that a crowd of nosey onlookers had started to form. People in the projects loved to gossip, and Chris was giving them a show.

"So what is wrong with me having a boyfriend?" I asked.

"What's wrong with it?" Chris replied "You are a boy, fool! Not a fucking girl, so get that straight in your head!"

"I am a girl in a boy's body," I defended myself. "It ain't my fault God made a mistake!"

A few of the adults standing close by started to mumble and murmur. I heard one man tell a woman that we were "Pastor Gloria's kids" and the lady said, "I guess Gloria's family ain't so perfect after all."

Chris turned to the couple, then back to me. "You see? You hear what they are saying about our family? You are a freak to them! No one cares about the so-called 'mistake' that God made. Shit, there ain't no God in the projects!" he proclaimed. "Mom must have been doing drugs when she was carrying your Black ass!"

Teka had heard enough. "That's your little sister, and she is my girlfriend! Family comes first; that is what I was taught," she affirmed. "If you don't want to love Sirbrian for who she is, then fuck all of y'all," she exclaimed, looking past my brother to address the others who had gathered. Teka turned around and hugged me, as did the other girls I was friends with. They had come over when Chris started yelling.

It was an emotional moment, and I started to cry. I removed Prince from my pocket and gave him a kiss. Chris said immediately, "What the hell? Did you just kiss your toy, man? I'm done. I ain't fighting for your ass no more. You better hope the babysitter lets you out because I sure as hell ain't going to," he said as he started to drag me by my shirt towards our building.

The next day, I was sitting by the window in my living room, watching the girls jump rope on the street. I wasn't even sad that I couldn't go out to join them. I was becoming proud of my new identity; I knew that, soon enough, I'd be back outside playing with the girls. Besides, I needed some quality time with my Prince. Before I stepped into my make-believe world, I checked to make sure Chris and Miss Tina were occupied. Then I strolled into my castle and Prince and I began to dance. I was happy to spend some much-needed quality time with him. All of a sudden, I noticed his smile had turned into a frown. I sat on the toilet and asked, "Prince, why do you look so sad? Did I do something to hurt you?"

Prince then responded, "Yes, my love. You promised to always make me a part of your world."

Upset and confused, I said, "Prince, I thought I had been keeping my promise. I would never do anything to hurt you."

The Boy of Hearts

Prince asked, "Are you ashamed to love me in your world? Why must we hide and be a secret when we are together? You aren't worth anything to me if I can't share you with the world. You'd rather suffocate me in your pocket wherever we go than let me meet your friends. You call this love?"

"I understand, Prince," I said. "What you don't realize is that if I'm seen spending time with you in that other world, people will tease and make fun of me. If they knew I was in love with a toy man, I'd be seen as a freak. I'm scared that someone will harm you or take you away from me," I contended.

"I want to be able to say that my princess looks beautiful with her makeup on," Prince started. "What is wrong with a prince saying that to his princess in front of others?"

Prince had a good point, and so did I. I knew we both had to be open-minded if our relationship was going to last.

"Prince, you know I have no choice but to spend more time in reality than in our make-believe world together, right?" I asked.

"Then why did you create our world, my princess?"

"I needed a world that accepts me as the girl I am inside," I replied, "instead of the boy that everyone sees."

Then Prince spoke softly, saying, "Let me go, Princess. Let me go on my way. You don't need our make-believe world anymore. You even said it yourself," continued Prince. "You spend more time on Earth than here with me. You created this world because you thought you could never find someone on Earth that would accept you for you. But in the time since our relationship began, your wish came true. Now you have Teka and the girls, right?" he asked.

"I do," I said. I knew Prince was right.

"As long as you continue to love yourself for who you really are, you will never stop being that girl at heart. No matter what anybody puts you through, the love in our hearts will last forever. No matter how far apart we are," he said.

"Prince," I started, "are you saying this is goodbye?"

"Yes," said Prince. "There is someone out there searching for your love, and someday they will find you," he said.

"So you're saying there's freaks like me out there, looking for another freak to love?" I asked.

"Don't call yourself a freak!" Prince snapped back. "Do you understand?"

"Yes, but you really think there's someone who wants me for me?" I asked.

The Boy of Hearts

"I said yes," Prince assured. "But the only way he's going to find you is if you stay true to who you are. Let the world see who you really are."

Prince was right, but I felt so sad. "Does this mean goodbye forever?" I asked with tears starting to roll down my cheeks.

"Don't cry, Princess," Prince said. "I will always be with you in spirit."

"Thank you, Prince," I said. "It really means a lot to me."

Prince then spoke up once more. "I need you to do something for me," he said. "I want you to get rid of me. Doing so will symbolize you letting go of your fears and facing the world independently. I want you to flush me down the toilet. Can you do that?" he asked.

I was reluctant. "I guess I could," I said, feeling very unsure.

"Sirbrian, you must!" said Prince. "Do it."

So I kissed him goodbye for one last time and flushed him down the toilet. To my surprise, my mother was standing in the doorway; she had heard the whole conversation. She just stood there, arms crossed. I couldn't imagine what Mom was going to do, but I figured the worst she could do was give me a whoopin'. Either way, I remember thinking it wasn't going to stop me from being me.

"Take off my clothes from your body and wash that mess off your face, young man!" Mom yelled. She had caught me in the bathroom. Before I could say anything, she ducked out of the doorway. She reappeared a moment later and started to splash me with prayer oil. I felt the burn as it went right into my eyes and down my face. I begged her to stop when she suddenly went to her knees. She looked into my eyes as I wiped off the oil.

"I swore that I gave birth to a healthy baby boy. Am I wrong, Sirbrian?" she asked. "Why are you doing this?"

I had to tell her the truth. "In my heart, I am a girl. I was born into a boy's body. God made a mistake, Mom. Can you ask Him to fix it? We all make mistakes, right, Mom?"

"People make mistakes, Sirbrian, not God."

I responded confidently, "No, Mom, God really did make a mistake. I don't belong in this body." I became frightened by the unusual look on her face.

"Devil," she said. "Remove yourself from my son's body. I am asking politely. You don't want to be on the bad side of a pastor," she said.

"Mom, I'm not a Devil," I cried.

"I know of your evil, deceitful ways. Be gone, Devil!" she yelled.

The Boy of Hearts

"This is why I keep my true self from you, Mom," I explained. "I knew you'd think I'm a freak," I cried as I finished removing my mother's clothes.

My mom then filled the tub, picked me up, and placed me into it. What she did next is inexplicable, and if I'd known what she was thinking I would have bit her. Without warning, she began to dunk me under the water. I hit my head on the tub and started to feel pain as I fought for air.

"Son, Mommy must drown you now. I have to kill the Devil living inside your body," she insisted. She continued to drown me while assuring me it was all God's plan and that I would awake when it was all over, cleansed of the evil spirit.

I was fighting for my life, kicking and punching, doing whatever I could to loosen my mom's grip. I tried to slow down my thoughts and keep from panicking. There must be something I can grab to hit her with, I thought. I reached my hand out of the tub, searching desperately. I felt a washcloth and a toothbrush, then finally a shampoo bottle. I gripped the bottle tightly and aimed at my mother's face. I hit her with it and the shampoo spewed from the bottle and all over my mother.

She released her vicious grip and began to scream. I came up for air while splashing her face full of water. I ran to Chris' room, naked and panicking. Chris jumped up to protect his game console from getting wet. "Get out of here!" he screamed, throwing me out into the hallway. Dad wasn't home from work yet. What was I to do? I just wanted to escape.

Mom approached me a few seconds later. She acted like nothing had happened. "Sirbrian, why are you sitting outside of Chris's door?" she asked with eerie calm, soap suds dripping from her hair. "Do you need a towel?" she asked. She offered me one and said, "Come to my room with me."

I followed suspiciously, but when we got to the room she began to dry me with care. Mom's hot comb was within arm's reach, plugged into the wall. If she tried to hurt me again, I would grab the comb and burn her in self defense. Did Mom share a body with another evil spirit? It felt like there was a side to her that wanted me dead.

Chapter 3

Secrets and Nightmares

Mom sat in her rocking chair, reading her Bible. A few days had passed since the drowning attempt. I was at the window, watching the girls jump rope and the boys play tag. I could actually hear our neighbors, the Freemans, talking about our family in the apartment next door. "How dare Gloria call herself a child of God," I heard Mrs. Freeman say, "More like a Devil in a wig. I think she tried to drown that boy the other day. I know what I heard," said Mrs. Freeman. "Maybe we should call the police--"

"Don't do it," said Mr. Freeman. "That ain't gonna accomplish anything, and everyone will just speculate that it was us who called. Getting in other folks' business is how you get murdered here," he added.

"That poor child," Mrs. Freeman said. "What if Gloria has some sort of breakdown, with the cheating and all?" she said.

"We don't need any of that getting back to her. Then she'll know we aren't really her friends," Mr. Freeman said.

"Shit, I guess telling could really bring the Devil out of her. Then she'll want to come over and kill us!" Mrs. Freeman said.

"We ain't getting involved!" hollered Mr. Freeman. "If you do, you can stay here with the bills. I'll pack my bag and be gone!"

Before I even heard the Freemans' conversation, I'd considered telling Teka about the abuse. I knew nobody else would really care, but maybe she would come and defend me. The words "Devil in a wig" frightened me; there was no way that Teka could fight Mom and win. What if Mom murdered Teka? I wouldn't be able to live with myself if that happened. Several times, I thought about calling the police myself. But would they even come? I decided to keep the child abuse to myself.

But one day, Dad came home a little earlier than usual. He was at the kitchen sink, washing paint from his hands while the news was on TV. "Dad, I know what the word faggot means," I blurted out.

"Who taught you that word?!" he yelled. "How dare you say that word in this house! You're supposed to be a child of God! God doesn't like ugly! If you talk like that, God may take our blessings away. Is that what you want?" Saying that word really set my father off.

"We were once very poor and lived in a shelter, but we kept our faith and prayed to God. That is the only reason our prayers were answered. It's not the best place we could be, but it's better than sleeping in one room on the floor or on cots, with strangers stealing what little you have," he continued.

"Well Dad, I'm a faggot. I'm a boy on the outside but a girl on the inside. When I grow up, I'm going to marry a man and make clothes for other faggots like me."

Dad became enraged. "What did I say about using that word?!" he yelled as he charged towards me.

I dodged him, ducking around the kitchen table. He tried to spank me but couldn't get to me. "Use the word 'gay,' not 'faggot'! Do you hear me?" He gave up on trying to get to me.

"Am I gay, dad?" I asked as we both caught our breath.

"No, son," he replied, "you're just going through a phase."

"Dad, what's a phase?"

"It's something you will grow out of as you get older," he replied.

"So are you saying that I can wear makeup anytime I want, until one day I won't want to wear it anymore?" I asked curiously.

The Boy of Hearts

"Why would I want you to do that?" he asked.
"So God can be mad at our family and take away
our blessings?"

Then I asked, "Does this mean you are going to
try and drown me? Or burn me with lighters pressed to
my feet? Or punch me, like Mom does?"

"Hey!" he exclaimed, "You watch your mouth.
We don't lie in this house. Don't you dare lie about
your Mom like that!" Dad was speechless as I
stripped down out of my clothes and showed him
my bruises. He began to cry as he dragged his fingers
across my fresh bruises, my skin cut open to the white
meat. I wriggled in pain as he examined my sores.
His sadness turned to rage quickly as he made his
way over to my mother. Enraged, he grabbed her by
the neck, squeezing the life out of her before our very
eyes. Stunned, she grabbed his hand with both of hers
and tried to pry his fingers loose. Then, with all the
strength in her legs, she kicked Dad off of her. He fell
backward into the nightstand, knocking over a lamp.
Gasping for air, Mom got to her feet.

My dad confronted her, asking about my bruises.
With the best acting performance I'd ever seen from
her, she lied to my dad's face. I remember wishing my
father had broken her neck as she told the lies right
in front of me. "Listen to me! I am not the one who
put those bruises on him! Think first before you jump
to conclusions. I am your wife. For how many years
now? Sirbrian is causing those wounds to himself. I
told him that God doesn't like ugly and that what he's
doing is an abomination," she said.

Dad wasn't really buying it. "Woman," he yelled, "Do I look like I was born yesterday? You are a pastor! A pastor! I know you take the Lord seriously. So seriously that if you thought one of your children was gay, you would do this to his body. Shit, you'd probably do it to break a curse or something!"

Mom was stern in her reply, stating, "We live in the hood! The hood! We are surrounded by gangs and violence! These gangs try to brainwash these kids into believing that children like our son are freaks! And that freaks like that should get their asses kicked," yelled Mom, now clenching a lamp for self defense in case Dad went at her again.

"I mean, that could be right. I used to beat up on gays when I was a kid, too," Dad said. "But our son doesn't need to lie about a damn thing! So why is he all of a sudden coming to me with these bruises, saying that you are torturing him?" he asked.

"Kids are probably beating him up for acting so flamboyant, with the crayon on his face!" she suggested. "He's acting like a damn girl! Did Sirbrian tell you that? Did he?! I bet he didn't, and that's why he's making up these stories! I never abused him! I cannot believe you put your hands on me, the woman who loves you!" she cried.

Dad was now even more confused as he turned to look at me. "Dad, she's lying!" I pleaded. "You have got to believe me! Mom really does have a dark side!" I pleaded. "You told me that your job is to protect me, Dad. That if I was ever in danger, I should tell you! Mom is going to kill me, and you don't even care!"

But Dad chose to believe his wife, and from that day on he saw everything I said as a bald-faced lie.

Summer came to an end and a new school year arrived. Our family drama was the hot topic of the projects. My mother's reputation had been damaged, and she resigned her position as the church pastor. Many of the church's members lived in our building and made it well known that she was the mother of a faggot.

As for me, I was proud to be the source of the rumor. A thousand of Scripture readings couldn't break the 'curse' of me being gay. My mom, once a respected pastor in our community, was disgraced.

My mother discarded most of my shorts and short sleeve shirts, even though we were still experiencing hot days that fall. I was forced to wear pants and long sleeve shirts so she could abuse me in even more places.

One particular day, I was awoken by my mother rummaging through my closet and dresser drawers. She tore up my room before finally finding what she was looking for. "Motherfucker, when I get done with you, you're gonna be scared to even look at crayons!" she screamed, throwing several of the crayons she'd found in the drawer at my head. She began to fill a sock with crayons as I watched her carefully. "You are not a girl! You just can't get that through your head, can you?" she said as she began to beat me with the crayon-filled sock.

"I'm a girl!" I proclaimed. "It's God's fault! God made me special, different from all His children!" I cried as I took punishment to my back, chest, and arms. Mom's powerful hits dropped me to the floor, where she jumped on me as a gorilla would do. She continued beating me senseless with the sock.

"Say you are a boy!" she yelled. "A boy that plays with trucks and wrestles with other boys!" As much as the punishment hurt, I refused to give in to her.

"I am a girl! A girl who plays with a tea set and loves double dutch! I was a princess in a make-believe world! I was married to a prince, one who loved me for me!" I cried out in pain as I suffered through my mother's vicious attack. There was no one there to save me. It was a very helpless and hopeless feeling. Dad had already left for work and Chris always had his door shut with the TV up so loud, a stampede wouldn't disturb him.

The next thing I remember, I was in the front seat of Mom's car on the way to school. I thought: The people in the other cars who can see into ours could never guess that this woman is beating me so bad. Mom showed no sympathy whatsoever. Instead, I was forced to listen to words a child should never have to hear from their mother.

"You listen to this!" she said. "If it gets out in any way to your teachers that I'm doing this to you, they will tell me. And if that happens, I'll start on your brother too, do you hear me?"

The Boy of Hearts

I nodded my head in agreement and asked her to never abuse Chris like this. I promised to keep it a secret, thinking about all the times when Chris had stood up for me. There was no way I could ever let what was happening to me, happen to him. He didn't deserve this torture; no one did.

In school, I kept up my good grades. I was also good at keeping Mom's secret. When we drew pictures, I even drew mine of a happy family with smiles on their faces. I spoke highly of my mother, trying to start false rumors about our healthy relationship so no one would suspect child abuse. At the end of every day, when school was over, I was smiling on the outside but crying on the inside. It was sad for me to watch the other children run to their parents, excited to see them. It was worse to see the parents embracing their kids with arms wide open and big smiles on their faces. I recall my friend Kenny had the best mom ever. I would have done anything to have lived with her. I remember clearly one particular conversation Kenny had with his mother.

"Hey, little man! How is my favorite son in the world?" Kenny's mom smiled at him as she spoke.

"Mom, I am the only son you have!" Kenny replied.

"You make me so proud to be your mom, that's why I say it all the time. Do you want me to stop saying it?" she asked. "I will if you want me to."

"No, Mom, I never said that. Call me your favorite son forever," Kenny smiled as she lifted him into her arms, hugging and kissing him.

"Well, it looks like you were a good boy in school today. What happens when you have a good day at school?" she asked.

"Ice cream!" Kenny exclaimed.

"That's right," Kenny's mom said. "Don't tell your dad!"

Then came my mother, armed with her fake smile, trying to give off the impression that she was part of a happy family. I knew that as soon as I got home, I was getting beat. All because she wanted to break this so-called 'curse.' The way she hugged me and kissed me and talked to me in front of people made me sick with how inauthentic it was. I desperately wanted to pull away and expose her for what she was! But her power over me was too strong. As we walked to the car, Mom would give me the look--that "Don't you dare!" look.

On the ride home, she would tell me in detail the things she was going to do to me. A normal conversation between us would go something like this:

"I see you are doing a good job of keeping our secret," she'd say. "You must really love your brother."

"I do," I would reply.

"Why does he love you? He should be beating your ass everyday."

Some days she would catch me with crayon on my face. "What is that on your face?!" she'd yell. "You'd better knock that shit off! How do you expect me to react to you looking like a freak? You just want to embarrass your family, don't you?"

I would assure her that I was not, in fact, trying to embarrass our family. I told her about Prince and how he made me promise to show everyone how beautiful I could be.

"Prince?" she'd ask sarcastically. "You talking about that toy man you talk to?"

"Yes, Mom, it helps me," I'd explain.

"I just want my son back," she'd say. "God, why can't I have him back? Release the demon from my son!"

"Mom, there is no demon inside me!" I insisted.

"Shut up! Just shut up!" she screamed. "God, please tell me that there is a way to break this curse. Send me a sign, oh Lord my God!" she continued. "I promise to obey you, Lord!"

As we got closer to the projects on the ride home from school, I would feel the tension and anxiety begin to take over. Tears would form in my eyes as I washed the crayon from my face, and I'd think about what Mom was about to do to my body. I was scared. I had been beaten to the white meat, tied up, stuck with pins, and nearly drowned. I had been through a lot, but I wasn't sure how much more I could take. Mom was doing everything she could to break this so-called 'curse.' Sometimes I thought about lying and telling Mom that her son was back and the curse had been lifted. Maybe this would stop the abuse against me. However, my heart would not give in. I made a promise to myself and to Prince that I would love myself, no matter what happened.

One day, when we had pulled up to the projects on the way back from school, we noticed old Mr. Terry watching us. He was a fat, nosey old man who always had something negative to say. As we approached the building, Mr. Terry rudely said, "Pastor Gloria, how does it feel to have a faggot as a son? I thought there was a God! What do you have to say about that, you fake ass preacher? If God has blessed you so much, then how come He can't fix your son? Huh? Instead of blessing you, He cursed you!" Mr. Terry's sarcastic insults got the attention of others standing by. They looked at me in confusion, noticing I had dried tears and smeared crayon on my face.

"My son is not a faggot! And that on his face is paint! We just came from a birthday party! God doesn't make mistakes when He creates!" she yelled for all to hear.

"Pastor Gloria, there you go lying. We know damn well you just came from picking that boy up from school. That's where he painted his face. Why can't you just accept that your son is a faggot?" Mr. Terry asked as we pushed through a crowd of people towards the entrance.

Mom dragged me up the stairs and my head banged the banister along the way. I leaned backwards, trying to release her grip on my arm. Mom was strong, and the more I struggled, the harder she gripped. I would try to bite her on occasion, but a slap across the face would be the only result.

How can I break free? I thought. If she got me behind a closed door, I knew what was to come. Will this be the time she kills me? I thought. I even punched and kicked doors to try to get the attention of someone who could help. Why is no one answering? I asked myself. Was everyone minding their business, just like the Freemans had? Once inside the door, my eyes scanned the apartment for Dad or Chris. Somebody had to be here who could save me. From across the hall, I heard a television. So Chris was home, but he was in his room with the door shut and the TV turned up really loud. As Mom pushed me towards my room, I began to think about the torture I was about to experience. I knew that during the abuse, I would completely zone out. I would try to escape mentally to avoid feeling such great pain. I would picture myself in another land, far away from that apartment and these projects. But I could never truly escape, not even in my dreams.

When the child abuse against me began, I started to have a reccuring nightmare. The dream started with Mom and me, stuck in traffic. Out the window, I saw children in nothing but their underwear. Their bodies were covered in bruises and their eyes cried blood. They would surround our car, banging on it as their cries grew louder. The cars surrounding us were filled with blood. I'd hear children's voices repeating, "Home is not where you want to go!"

In one car, there was a child dressed like a pastor. He had no eyes. He was repeating: "Where are you going to go?"

Then suddenly, my car started to fill up with crayons. I felt my seat belt getting tighter and tighter so that I couldn't open the door. Blood started to spray from my pores all over the inside of the car. Suddenly, it went dark.

When the light came back on, I could see myself being tied to a bed by angels as I struggled to get free. I was in a dark bedroom, dimly lit by candles on a dresser and a nightstand. Suddenly, it went dark again and I awoke. I sat up, drenched in sweat, tightly wrapped in my sheets.

The nightmares persisted for many nights. If I could have chosen to stay awake forever, I would have. My mind just couldn't erase these nightmares.

Mom always made sure to abuse the parts of my body that were hidden to the world. The last thing she wanted was for anyone to know she was a child abuser. But one day, a phone call to our residence changed all of that.

The Boy of Hearts

Mom was in the kitchen, frying chicken, when the phone suddenly rang. "Get the phone, Sirbrian!" Mom yelled. Having Mom ask me, a seven-year-old, to answer the phone made me feel special. It was a responsibility I had never been given before.

"Okay, Mom, I'll answer it!" I said excitedly. I wanted to show Mom that I could answer the phone like an adult. I had just colored my lips with purple crayon and had put on one of Mom's wigs. So, I was in full girl mode as I answered the phone.

"Hello, God is good, can I ask who is speaking?" I said politely, just how Mom would have.

"God is good, you're right about that," said a man on the other end of the line. "Is Pastor Gloria there?" he asked.

"Who's calling?" I asked.

"This is Ron," the man replied, "Tell her it's urgent."

"I'm sorry, Mr. Ron. Pastor Gloria, who is my mom, is busy at the moment. But I will tell her that you called," I said.

Mr. Ron then said, "I didn't know Pastor Gloria had a daughter! What's your name?" he asked.

"No, that's okay, I'd rather keep my name to myself," I replied. "God bless, goodbye!" I said rather nervously.

I heard a noise behind me. As I turned, I received a punch to my left eye. Mom had struck me so hard that I was blinded; my left eye is still blind from that blow to this day. She followed the first strike up with two more, this time to my right eye. The sight of me wearing her wig must have enraged the woman to a point of losing control. I dropped the phone, trying to flee. As I ran, I tripped over the coffee table and fell to the floor as Mom stood over me. I was in so much pain that, for a moment, I thought for sure Mom was going to hug me and say she was sorry.

Instead, she punched me in the stomach and threw me over the couch. Mom jumped on top of me like a raging gorilla. She hit me over and over as I tried to cover my face. The punches were coming harder and harder, when suddenly I heard a voice.

"Sirbrian! Sirbrian, do you hear me?" it said.

"Yes," I replied. "Who are you?"

The voice replied, "My name is Devon. I am a spirit, and I've become part of your body. I've been created by the pain you are enduring. I'm here to help you, Sirbrian."

Chapter 4

Another Goodbye

The next thing I knew, I awoke.

"You're punching our body, Sirbrian," Devon said.

I was confused. "Our body?" I asked. Then, I noticed I was punching myself all over; nothing could make me stop.

"Yes," he responded. "We now share the same body. What you are experiencing is a post traumatic episode."

"How do I stop punching myself?" I asked.

"Think of a happy place," Devon assured me.

Immediately, I started to think about Prince. "I'm thinking about being a princess dancing at the ball with my prince. I am the most beautiful princess in all of the land. My lips are colored red and my eyelids are blue, the same blue as my long, flowing dress," I shared.

"Great!" Devon said. "Now imagine your world is dark. Is it pitch dark yet, Sirbrian?"

"Yes," I replied.

"Now open your eyes."

"Okay," I said. "Where are you?" I sat up in bed, tied up in sweaty sheets. I looked down at my bloody hands, now more afraid of myself than I was of Mom. Could Mom have been right all along? Did the Devil really control my body?

I walked into the bathroom and looked at myself in the mirror. I wiped my hands across the bruises, wondering if I could ever be beautiful again. I started to color them with crayons before slamming the crayons into the sink. It was no use. I would be ugly forever. I then punched the mirror in frustration, shattering it instantly. My hands were already numb from punching myself, so I felt no pain. Suddenly, I heard Mom calling from another room, yelling about all the commotion.

"God, what did I do to deserve this life?" I cried, throwing my head back and looking at the ceiling. At that moment, I heard a voice.

It said, "Relax, Sirbrian. Close your eyes and count back from five. Let me take over your body now." The voice was Devon, who again assured me that he was no Devil. He told me he was there to help, so I agreed to give over control of my body to him once again.

"I will help you to stand up to your mother, Sirbrian," he said. There was a sinister tone to his voice as he said, "We will show her how it feels to be abused."

He continued by demanding, "Help me to take control of your mind and heart. Once you hand it over to me, you will see the power we can wield." So I closed my eyes and began to concentrate on my breathing. I counted back from five, and when I made it to one I felt a strange sensation take over my body. I felt strong and confident. Mom had finally met her match!

Devon began punching the mirror, shattered glass falling into the sink. I felt no pain as several pieces stuck into my hands and arms, drawing blood. As one, Devon and I darted from the bathroom, down the hall, and into the kitchen where Mom was watching the local news and preparing dinner. She had her back to us as Devon made us pull a chair from the table, placing it behind my mother. We backed up several yards and then, running at full speed, we hopped onto the chair and leaped onto Mom's back. With pieces of mirror in our hands, we stabbed at her, cutting through her shirt and into her skin.

The Boy of Hearts

Mom screamed, "Ahh! What the fuck are you doing!?"

We continued to stab, showing no mercy. Devon was so strong that he had us pull Mom to the ground. He made us grab the pot of hot grits from the stove and stand menacingly over her. Mom's face was in such utter disbelief that for a moment, I tried to take back control of the body. Devon resisted, yelling, "She's going to get what she deserves!" Devon was now angrier than ever. He had us pour the hot grits onto her, slamming the metal pot onto the side of her head. Mom yelled out in pain: "My face! Oh my God, Sirbrian!"

"Who's Sirbrian?" Devon bellowed. "Last time I checked, my name was Devon!" he said as we continued assaulting her with the pot. Blood sprayed from Mom's mouth, but this only made Devon push us harder. He wanted to kill her.

Suddenly, as if she was taken over by another entity, Mom rose to her feet. She wiped the grits from her eyes, grabbed us by the neck, and tossed us across the table. All of the pots and pans on the table top clanged to the floor. The commotion was so loud that Chris heard it over the blaring of his TV in the next room. He ran into the kitchen, his eyes wide in astonishment at what he was seeing. Blood and grits were splattered across the floor. Both Mom and I were bleeding.

Mom grabbed a rolling pin and started to come at me, prompting Chris to take action. He reached for the phone, dialing 911. Mom chased me around the table, rolling pin in hand. She was going to murder me. Chris began to speak into the phone, panicked by what he was seeing.

"My mom is trying to kill my little brother!" he wailed. "He's bleeding!" After a short pause, Chris continued to answer questions from the dispatcher. "East Falls Projects, on the corner of Chew Street and East Fall Avenue!" I heard him yell, "Apartment 1425!"

Mom seemed so unfazed. "For five years, this Devil has controlled my son's body!" she yelled. "I'm not going to tolerate it. What does the Devil want with my son?!"

After Chris hung up, he came to my aid. He blocked our mother as she attempted to get to me with the rolling pin. Suddenly, I felt weak as blood continued to drip down my chest and arms. I must have fainted, because the next thing I knew I was on the couch, sore all over, with Chris leaning over me in tears. Chris had stopped the bleeding with rags and applied bandaids. Devon apparently had released my body back over to me. I watched absently as Mom was handcuffed and escorted out of our apartment.

"Devon, are you there?" I asked softly.

"I'm here," he replied, "and I always will be. I'll do whatever it takes to protect our body. Love who you are, Sirbrian. Keep your promises to Prince and, more importantly, to yourself."

The Boy of Hearts

"How do you know about the deal I made with Prince?" I asked curiously.

"There's a lot of things I know about you," Devon said.

"Devon?" I asked. "Do you think Chris and I are going away, like to a foster home?"

"Probably so," he replied.

"Do you think I can take my crayons with me?" I asked.

"I don't see why not," he replied.

"I'm gonna miss you, Devon," I said with deep emotion.

"No you won't," he assured me, "because I'll be right there with you, sharing our body."

Devon gave me hope and strength. He gave me confidence. As long as I had Devon, I could take on the world--no matter where the journey might take us.

Chris changed after that night. He began to embrace me as his little sister and assured me he would protect me from bullies. "You were right all along," he said, "about being a girl trapped in a boy's body."

From that day on, I became me. I felt freedom at last, since I knew my big brother would be there to protect me in the next chapter of our lives.

The next day, we received a visit from the Department of Human Services. Two stocky white men, dressed in suits and armed with credentials, came to our apartment. "Is your father home?" one of the men, whom I'd know later as Jack, asked.

Chris responded sharply, "Who wants to know? You guys are quick to take a lil nigga out the projects, aren't you?"

"Little man," the man I'd later know as Fred said, "I respect that you want to protect your little brother."

"First of all, that's my sister, not my brother," Chris said confidently, his chest puffed out and hands balled up. "Second of all, our father is not home."

The two men asked us to step out into the hallway as they asked us a slew of questions. Jack then stepped aside for a moment, pulled out his phone briefly, and then returned. "Fred," he said, "I'm going to check in with the neighbors." Jack knocked on the door of the closest neighbors, the Freemans. Fred followed behind; the door opened and the officers introduced themselves.

"How well do you know the Spease family?" Jack asked.

Other tenants began to open their doors to see the action. Mr. Freeman wanted confirmation that Mom was in jail before he shared any information. Jack and Fred assured him that she was. Then, Mr. and Mrs. Freeman began to chirp like a couple of birds.

The Boy of Hearts

"These walls are paper thin," Mrs. Freeman stated. "I could hear the little one, Sirbrian. He would be playing make-believe." Jack and Fred looked at each other; they seemed very interested.

Mrs. Freeman continued, "Then I'd hear Gloria, screaming and yelling. I know she was beating that poor boy. I care about those kids like they are my own grandchildren, but I didn't ever say anything. I wanted to help protect Gloria's reputation, you know." Jack and Fred began to write down everything the Freemans said in their notepads.

"Word on the street was that Pastor Gloria's son was a faggot. I believe she couldn't accept that her life wasn't perfect after all. This caused her to have a mental breakdown," Mr. Freeman said.

Fred's eyebrows raised as he asked, "What do you mean by 'mental breakdown,' Mr. Freeman?"

"I think she thought that boy was cursed, and she was hellbent on curing him. I would hear that boy scream bloody murder, let me tell you. He must have been having nightmares, too, because I'd hear him kicking and screaming at all hours of the night."

The officers asked a few more questions, then wrapped up the interview. They turned to us and ordered us to follow them. But before we could, the Freemans stepped in to give Chris and me their blessings.

"Kids," Mrs. Freeman started, "You're not babies anymore. You've both been through a lot, but it will only make you stronger. Other kids will look at you both and see hope that they can get through their own struggles as well." Mrs. Freeman's eyes began to water as she knelt down to hug me. "Promise me you will pray every night before you go to sleep. Pray for us, and we'll pray for y'all. You kids have to be strong, you hear?"

We assured her we would be and then we followed the officer's orders to grab a few things and follow them. We both felt reluctant to leave, especially because Dad wasn't home yet. Jack and Fred sensed that we weren't ready to leave, but they insisted we would be safer with them and that we didn't have a choice in the matter. The officers believed that because our father let the abuse go on, he wasn't equipped to take care of us.

Soon enough, I had my crayons and pocket mirror and Chris had his game. There was nothing left to do, so we stepped outside our apartment to surrender ourselves to the two men. It was a surreal feeling as we made our way down the steps and out of the apartment building. I smiled as I thought about the good times I'd had in the projects, laughing and playing with my girlfriends and dancing in the bathroom with Prince.

As we stepped out into the sunshine, I saw the girls jumping rope. Teka smiled brightly at me. "Hey girl," she yelled, "come jump rope one more time before you leave!"

I pulled on Fred's arm. "Can I?" I asked excitedly.

The Boy of Hearts

"Sure, go ahead," Fred said. It seemed like the whole project was out that day, cheering me on. I took comfort in knowing that everyone would remember me for me. I hugged the girls for the last time and made my way to the cruiser. A new journey lay ahead. Would the people in my new life accept me for who I am? I thought. Only time would tell.

I'll never forget that drive on the way to St. Joseph's House for Boys. Jack and Fred mocked my mother for being a pastor. "Looks like she's the one who has a demon," one of them said. "I'll tell ya, the boy gave her a run for her money this time. Didn't he?"

I thought they must be referring to the cuts and bruises on Mom's body, the ones that Devon had put there. "Sirbrian! You just be you, little man," Fred said. "Your mother was wrong for not letting you express yourself for who you are. You said she's never seen a gay person before? That's ridiculous," he added.

I remember sitting in the back seat of the cruiser as Jack flipped through radio stations, trying to find the perfect tunes for our listening pleasure. I picked up a piece of paper left in the back seat. I folded the paper as best I could into a paper man. I began to daydream that Prince was with me in the car. I imagined that we were riding in a horse-drawn carriage on the way to a grand castle. Four white horses led the way as we headed to the royal ball. I had to be pretty for the ball, so I took out my crayons and mirror and began to apply makeup to my lips and eyes. In no time, I had transformed from a battered Black boy from the hood into a beautiful princess. I hoped that Prince wouldn't notice the ugly bruises on my hands, face, and chest. As we drew closer to the castle, Prince suddenly appeared in front of me.

"Princess Sirbrian, you look just as beautiful as the day I first met you," said Prince. I blushed as I held Prince close to my chest. I wanted him to feel my heart beating, to feel the love I had for him.

I sat Prince across from me and he watched as I brushed my long, blonde hair with my solid gold brush. Suddenly, we hit a bump in the road and I was knocked back into reality. We weren't in the hood anymore; we were in a white neighborhood. I smiled as I admired the big, beautiful houses. I noticed a white father holding the seat of his daughter's bike, teaching her to ride it. I felt a wave of shame; I was almost ten years old and I still didn't know how to ride one.

Should I wave to the girl? I thought. No. She'll just think I'm a freak with this makeup and these bruises all over my body.

That's when Devon jumped in. "Don't ever disrespect yourself like that!" he cried out to me. "Bruises and scars will fade away."

I didn't fully trust Devon yet. I thought, Is he a Devil who attacked my mom, or is he just trying to help me?

Devon became angry. "I can read your thoughts," he said. "Why would you disrespect me this way?"

"I'm in a lot of pain!" I explained to Devon. "Maybe we shouldn't have done that to Mom."

"Should we have let our body die instead?" he said. "Your mother was trying to kill us!"

I thought, Maybe she really was trying to break a curse. If she had really gotten that close to killing us, God would have saved us. Right?

Devon was adamant, "God don't give two shits about you. If He did, He wouldn't have let you go through those years of abuse! Did you forget that I saved you from drowning in the tub? Or that I helped you escape your beatings? Any child would pay dearly to have my kind of powers," Devon said. He was right; he had come to my rescue so many times. Why did I still doubt him?

Just then, Devon said one last thing that made me realize my relationship with him was special. "You're beautiful, Sirbrian. Don't ever forget that." That statement gave me the confidence I needed to believe in him. Just then, we drove up to my and Chris's new foster home.

As we pulled in, I was impressed with how nice the place looked. It was a stone house, and the property had swings, jungle gyms and basketball hoops. There were tall trees all over, with friendly-looking squirrels running up and down them. I saw boys of all ages and races interacting together, playing games of tag and handball. Everyone looked happy.

Maybe this won't be so bad after all, I thought. As I stepped out of the car, I noticed that some children had stopped what they were doing. I caught a few of their awkward stares. Had they never seen a boy with different colors of crayon on his face?

I followed Jack, Fred, and Chris as we approached the front door. I walked inside and saw boys playing board games and watching cartoons on TV. My eyes searched the room, but not one of them had crayon on his face. Again, I felt the shame of looking different. I hoped nobody else would notice my appearance.

A man, whose name I'd later learn was Dan, approached us. He shook hands with Jack and Fred and looked Chris and me over. "Are these my new boys?" he asked.

"Yes," Jack replied. "This is Sirbrian. He's 'a girl in a boy's body,' so he says. And that's his brother, Chris."

"So, you're gay?" Dan asked me. I felt Chris tense beside me; I could tell he didn't appreciate the question. He stepped in between Dan and me, raising his voice to say: "Yeah, he's gay, and if a boy here has a problem with that, he'll have to deal with me!"

The Boy of Hearts

I smiled. Even if the boys here knew I was gay, Chris would protect me. And now, Mom couldn't even abuse me anymore.

"Discrimination is not tolerated here!" the man named Dan proclaimed. "Any boy who acts hatefully will be held accountable and will be punished."

"Your punishment ain't shit. I'll show these niggas punishment!" Chris yelled. He sure was wound up. Everything that had transpired over the last forty-eight hours suddenly boiled over for Chris. "A punishment ain't gonna stop one of these little boys from calling him a faggot." He turned to face the room. "Who got a problem with my little sister?" he asked loudly for all to hear. "Disrespect my sister and you will deal with me!"

Dan and all the boys in the room got the point. "Chris, let's just take it one day at a time," Dan proposed.

"I should have never let my mother hurt him," Chris said, looking down shamefully at the floor. Chris felt bad about the whole situation. But we'd agreed that we would get through this together, no matter the obstacles we might face.

While Dan finished processing our paperwork, I gazed out the window. In the reflection, I could see that the boys seemed to be having some type of meeting. Are they talking about me and Chris? I wondered. Maybe Devon can help me.

I began punching myself to get Devon's attention. I punched myself so hard that I got a nose bleed, but Devon did not answer.

"Please, Devon, Chris and I need you right now!" I pleaded. "I think the boys are planning to jump us!" I started to cry. As crayon smeared down my face and into my eyes, I whispered, "I'm sorry if I offended you."

Then I heard his voice: "You don't need me. I'm a Devil, remember?"

"No, you're not," I replied. "I understand better now."

Slowly, I felt Devon's power come back into my body.

"Thank you, Devon. I couldn't face them without you," I said.

"If you want this power, you gotta let me do what I'm gonna do. Don't tell me later that I went too far or some shit," Devon said. I nodded. Behind me, I was sure the boys were plotting something; they kept looking back at us with angry expressions.

Kevin, the longest-tenured boy in the home, approached me. He called me a fool and told me he ran this place. "You ain't gonna do that faggot ass shit up in here. We don't want you. Your own parents didn't even want you!" Kevin said. I was frightened, and I could feel that Devon had full control at this point.

"Tell DHS that you want foster care, not a group home. Save yourself an ass whoopin'," Kevin said.

"I ain't going nowhere, fool," Devon said in my voice. "You're in the way."

Kevin grew even more agitated. "Do you know who the fuck I am?" he asked. "I ain't that dude to disrespect, champ."

Then, out of nowhere, we kicked out the leg from the table and smacked Kevin right in the face. He dropped to the floor instantly. We jumped on top of him and continued to beat him mercilessly. Devon wouldn't stop, so I couldn't either. The other boys looked on, having no idea what to do. Devon had no remorse. He saw blood and wanted more. "Now you can be a pretty princess," Devon said, pulling out my crayons and my mirror and dropping them on Kevin's chest.

It was the ultimate mockery. I knew Kevin would stay out of my way from here on out.

Mr. Dan scurried over with a look of terror. "What happened? Kevin, what happened to your face?" he demanded.

Before Kevin could say anything, I said, "He leaned on the table and fell onto the floor."

"Stop all this bullshit! Tell me the truth, Kevin, or you'll be put on punishment," threatened Mr. Dan.

Kevin, like any boy from the hood, knew not to snitch or else he would get it again. So, Kevin did what he was supposed to do: he came up with the biggest lie he could to keep from bringing more harm to himself.

"Mr. Dan, I keep on telling you about how much we need real tables instead of these cheap fold-up ones. Look what happened! One of the legs came apart while we were arm wrestling on it! Shit! The table flipped up and cracked me upside the face! Got my face leaking with blood!" Kevin looked at me from out of the corner of his eye, afraid.

While Kevin was in the office being attended to, the body that Devon and I shared was the center of attention. The living room was filled with boys, each afraid that he was going to be beaten to death if he showed any homophobia towards us. We stood in the center of the floor with our chest poked out, proud to be feared by potential homophobes.

Would we be feared tomorrow? There was no way to know. All I could think at that moment was that I was being shown respect for the girl I was at heart.

Part II

Can a gay boy's dangerous
alter ego be kept under control?

Chapter 5

Interlude

I was now a 14 year-old, but not your average one. I was a gay teenager whose paranoia took over his mind, body and soul.

Why could I hear every conversation in the household crystal clear, even while I was walking around outside? It was the power that Devon had over our body. He was so eager to be aware of what was going on around us at all times. Nobody was going to catch us off guard. Not if Devon could help it.

Perfectly sharpened pencils and a container of floss were our companions wherever we went. Whether I was asleep or awake, they were always in my left pocket. Devon put them there, of course. He intended to use them as weapons to protect our body from the hard world of homophobia. I tried to get Devon to understand that Mr. Dan gave us no reason to believe that he wouldn't protect us from gay bashing. I was sure that if we let him know what was happening when it was happening, he would do something about it. But getting Devon to believe that anyone else was capable of protecting us was impossible.

Every time I tried to have this conversation with him, it led to an argument where he threatened to cause harm to our body if I tried to intervene on my own behalf. Through the eyes of my foster brothers, a fight like this with Devon would look like I was harming myself. It was a brutal scene that would only make them fear me more, giving me zero chance to ever receive love from them.

What I wouldn't give to push one of my younger foster brothers on the swing! I'd lift him up to the monkey bars and stand there watching him challenge himself by swinging through the whole obstacle course. It would mean the world to me to know that by standing there and watching him, I would give him confidence to do it.

"Look! Look! Sirbrian! Sirbrian! Look! I'm doing it!," he would say. He would stare at me, smiling, so proud to show an older foster brother that he was just as strong as anyone. This display would bring me to embarrass myself by crying. I'd be crying only happy tears, though, because for once I'd see that someone loved me because of how I made them feel inside. That someone wouldn't care that I was gay; it wouldn't matter at all to them.

I stared out the window at Tyrone, who was short and Hispanic. He was one of the younger foster brothers, trying to swing as high as the older ones, but he just didn't have what it took to do it on his own.

Just a single push would get him there. I thought, Maybe he doesn't know or understand what 'gay' means. He might see it as just a nickname.

I started heading out the door towards Tyrone in hopes of showing him what brotherhood was all about. As soon as I made it outside, there went the older boys. They were doing exactly what I knew they were going to do: they scattered away from the play area equipment. Some gave me looks of pure evil and others gave me looks of fear. Why wasn't Tyrone following them? He just continued swinging, enjoying the cool breeze that swinging produces. He paid the commotion no mind.

I could feel Devon trying his best to take control of our body; he made my hand clench the sharp pencils in my pocket. There were too many angry faces pointed toward us not to be prepared.

"Easy, Devon, easy," I pleaded with him. "Is this really what you want to do? Are you trying to take away the little happiness I have in life?" I was desperate.

"What should we choose: a couple minutes of happiness or hours of pain?" Devon said sternly. "Don't you remember when Mom would press those hot forks on our body?! How long were you in pain, Sirbrian?" he asked, doing his best to knock what he called 'sense' into my head.

"A long time," I whispered. "I was in pain because Mom burned me down to the white meat. But that was the past. Why even bring that up? Dr.

The Boy of Hearts

Tan said that not everyone takes gay bashing to the extreme." Dr. Tan was my therapist at St Joseph's, and I did my best to trust what he told me. "Anyway, these boys are scattering away from me, not approaching me," I said. Thank God only I could hear Devon at that time. It would seem from a distance that I was just talking to myself.

I could see that Devon was open-minded to what I said; he released his grip around the sharp pencils that were cutting holes on the inside of my pocket. The holes were big enough to stab me multiple times in the leg. I put pressure on my leg while my hand was in my pocket and stopped the bleeding for the moment.

"Hey, little man, you want a push?" I asked Tyrone cheerfully. I leaned over, resting my hands on my thighs.

"Yes! Why would I say no? Please tell me that you can do an underdog!" Tyrone said excitedly, bouncing up and down on the swing.

"Isn't that when I pull you back while you hold the swing as tight as you can, so far back that you are in midair over top of my head? Then, after holding the swing as high as I can, I race underneath you and you come down right behind me?"

"Yes, yes! That's it! That's it!! Can you do it? Can you do it?! Please? Please?! I am strong enough to hold on! Trust me, I am!" Tyrone begged.

I thought a push like that was too dangerous for Tyrone. I worried his arms were too fragile to hold on during such a wild ride. But how could I say no to such an innocent face? So I did what he asked for.

To my surprise, Tyrone had the strength to hold on. When the swing came to a stop, Tyrone was so proud of himself for withstanding what the older brothers could. He hopped off the swing and into my arms, knocking me to the ground. There, I tickled him and enjoyed watching him smile while I cried happy tears.

"Why are you crying, Sirbrian?" Tyrone asked, concerned.

"I am just happy that you are happy because I am making you happy," I replied with a grin. If this was what love felt like, then there was nothing I wouldn't do to receive more of it. It was summertime. What perfect timing for Tyrone to come into my life and accept me as his big brother!

The title of big brother came with great responsibility. I needed to be patient when teaching Tyrone how to ride a bike. In the times that he wanted to give up, I was right there to give him the confidence to try again. I showed him what would come of his persistence by doing wheelies and tricks on my bike. And after a month of bumps, bruises, and teary eyes, the day finally came that my little brother could ride a bike all by himself.

The Boy of Hearts

Of course, Tyrone couldn't wait until his teacher was wide awake to show what he had accomplished. I was dead asleep at seven in the morning when he came charging into my room to pull me out of bed. He was already dressed. What did it matter if I was still in my pajamas, with eye boogers in my eyes and morning breath stinking up the room?

Tyrone insisted for me to hurry with him. "I can do it now! I can do it now! Sirbrian, watch! You'll see!"

"Do what? Do what?! Boy, do you know what time it is?" I said, confused and half asleep.

He took me outside and sat me on the step. I saw his bike and instantly knew what this was about. It made me feel good inside, knowing that me watching him ride his bike by himself meant the world to Tyrone. There he was, riding in circles on his bike in the parking lot. He kept his eye on me, making sure I caught every moment.

"I can ride my bike on my own, look! Look, look!"

"I'm looking! Wow! See, and you thought you could never do it. See what happens when you practice every day?" I said with a grin, now wide awake.

"Teach me how to wheelie! Come on, get your bike out of the shed," Tyrone said so eagerly.

"Easy, little brother. We have all day for that. Hello? Can I take a shower first and eat?!" I said with happy sarcasm.

"Oh yeah, right! What am I doing?" Tyrone said with excitement.

So we both headed back into the house, leaving the bike in the parking lot. Little did I know I wouldn't have a lot of time to teach Tyrone how to wheelie. A week later, he got adopted by an Asian couple. Saying goodbye to Tyrone was the hardest thing I had ever done in my life at that time.

"Sirbrian, what are you doing? Pack all my bags on the left side, so we won't get confused about whose bag is whose when we get into our new house!" Tyrone said, excited.

"I am not going, little brother. Just you. I heard you have a little Asian brother there waiting to meet you," I said. I wasn't sure how to feel. I didn't want him to go, but at the same time I wanted the best for him.

"What do you mean, you're not coming?! Asian people, get away from me!" Tyrone said angrily while tearing himself from their arms and running into mine.

"It hurts me to say this, but: Tyrone, you deserve a family to love you. I can't be selfish. I love you with all my heart. You hear? Just because you are leaving me doesn't mean I am going to love you less or ever forget you." I said, trying not to look at Tyrone.

When I finally did look, I saw him gazing up at me in tears. I let loose the tears that I was holding back. All I could do was give him all the wisdom that I could find in myself at the moment.

"I look at every adult like my real Mom and Dad. Will these people turn my eyes black and blue like my real parents did, because I have a bad memory?" Tyrone asked.

What could I say to him after that? I sure didn't want to make a promise I couldn't keep.

"I will pray for you every night," I said to him. "I will ask God to keep you safe. Promise you will do the same! Do you remember everything I taught you, Tyrone?"

"Yes, Sirbrian."

"Take what I taught you. You are going to need it if you plan on being the best big brother. Now go and make me proud," I said, wiping tears from my face and putting Tyrone in the car.

While watching them drive off and out of sight, I could only say to myself that I would always love Tyrone. He would be missed. Devon must have felt my pain, a pain that brought out a side of him I never thought existed.

There I was, pushing a swing, remembering all the good times Tyrone and I shared. Then, out of nowhere, Devon lured me into having a conversation with him. "What I am about to say, Sirbrian, I hope you won't take as me being soft. I am far from that. I don't know where this is coming from, but I am happy for you. Tyrone showed me that there are some good heterosexuals out here after all. I only expect the worst and hope for the best because of where we once were," Devon explained with compassion.

"Thank you, Devon, that means a lot to me," I replied while giving myself a big hug. That was my way of hugging Devon.

Two boys were adopted that day, and I could only wish them the best. As soon as they left, two new boys arrived to fill their beds. Mike and Danny were their names. I would soon see these boys as a prime example of homophobia. They both got so deep under my skin.

I was snapped back into reality.

Chapter 6

Donna

I was now a 14 year-old, slim, Black, flamboyant gay teenager leaning on a first-floor hallway wall in the house. Resting my injured back, popping my blueberry bubblegum, and picking out my rainbow-dyed afro. Was that gay pride or what? Mike and Danny were disgusted by that. They were sitting on the floor in front of me, playing checkers while giving me dirty looks (of course.) Mike was a Black, overweight, nappy-headed boy. Danny was also Black, but skinny and too tall for his age. While waiting for his turn, Danny popped his pimples. Both boys made it their mission to show me how proud they were to humiliate me with homophobia in a physical manner--on a daily basis, if they could.

These were the two who moved into St. Joseph's House for Boys months ago, after living in the Diamond Street Project. Shit, it had to be the roughest project of all projects in Philadelphia. There, you had no choice but to hold onto the bannisters for dear life when coming and going. Bullets were always in your way when you walked down the steps in a housing development project. There were rats too full to move out of your way. These rats knew that humans were too busy worrying about whether they'd survive that day to see tomorrow.

Both boys came on the same day, and made it clear right away to Mr. Dan that he could take his rules and shove them up his ass. Only a gun pointed to their head was going to force them to follow some bullshit rules. I knew that I had to focus long and hard to keep my dangerous alter-ego Devon from crossing paths with them. Of course, the day finally came that my rainbow afro got their attention. While I was on the swing and they were playing catch, I pretended not to see them approach me.

"Faggot! Faggot boy! You hear me talking to your faggot ass! You snow-cone-headed motherfucker," Mike yelled out to me, aggravated because I chose to ignore him. I continued on swinging. On the way to me, Danny snatched up a handful of dirt from the ground. Foster boys who knew what I was capable of grew terrified while they dispersed in different directions. Those boys wanted to be far enough away to not be seen as a witness. I brought the swing to a stop. I was then in arm's reach of Mike and Danny and their big, balled-up, ashy lips. Out of nowhere, Danny threw a football at me. It hit me dead in the nose, busting it open.

"Damn, faggot boy, I would've thought your blood would've leaked out in different colors. The same colors in the motherfucking rainbow," said Danny, now choking me and holding me up by my shirt. While I still sat on the swing, Danny held me steady while Mike got behind me. He brutally wrapped the swing chain around my neck and pulled on it with all his strength in hopes of putting me to sleep. Danny poured the dirt from his hand onto my head, while I suffered miserable pain from the chain cutting deep into my neck. This woke up Devon, who was furious and needed an explanation. An outrageous conversation began between him and me--a conversation that Mike and Danny couldn't hear. It appeared to them that I was arguing with myself. How creepy was that?

"Who the fuck is choking us?! Give me the power to see out of one of our eyes! I need to see who our predator is! I need to figure out how to get out of this strangulation!" Devon demanded, furious. So I relaxed our body just a bit to give Devon the control to see out of one eye. Through it, he could see a hostile Danny choking me with my shirt while grinding his teeth.

Devon demanded, "Sirbrian! Release the body over to me! I have an idea of how I can get our body out of this!"

"Promise me you will not murder these boys. No matter how thuggish they are, at the end of the day they are just children," I said, gasping for air.

"Mike, you hear what Rainbow Boy is saying?" Danny asked. "'Promise me you will not murder these boys. No matter how thuggish they are!' Who the fuck is he talking to like that?!"

Danny, confused and distraught, choked me tighter.

"Danny, why would you ask a dumb ass question like that?! I don't fucking know. Maybe he is trying to tame a fairy demon inside of him!" laughed Mike. "Oh fairy demon, please don't come out and throw fairy dust on us!"

"Sirbrian, we're starting to feel faint! Like, what the fuck?! Let go of our body!" Devon said, panicked.

"Promise me first!" I said, indignant. "If you don't promise me, I guess this will be the moment that we die."

"Okay, I promise! Give it to me," cried Devon. I entered into a meditative state of mind and body, vulnerable enough for Devon to take complete control.

"Devon, give me control to see out of our right eye," I said.

Devon lifted our legs up and around Danny's ribs, where we clenched so tight that I could feel Danny's ribs breaking.

"My ribs are breaking! They're breaking! I can't breathe!" Danny yelled out in painful agony, trying to open our legs' powerful clench around his ribs.

"You, behind me! Let me go! Release our body, or your friend will suffer the consequences!" Devon said.

"Okay, okay! I'm off, I'm off! Please let him go!" Mike said, frightened for Danny's life. He released us and fell to the ground.

"How does it feel to have a few ribs broken?!" Devon asked the boys. No answer.

"You do not want to speak?! Then I will receive the answer I demand. What do you think about that?! When I break all your ribs, you will give me the answer."

Devon squeezed tighter and tighter until all Danny's ribs were broken. Devon's mighty clench was released and Danny sank to his knees. Mike stayed still, too petrified to move, while tears and snot poured into his open mouth. Devon kept his promise. This filled me with pride while I returned to having full control of the body.

While heading towards the house, I could sense that Mike and Danny didn't have to be told to keep this encounter a secret.

Later, while watching Danny and Mike play checkers, I grew sad. Would I ever be asked to play?

Two foster brothers walked past me, making their way out the front door to play baseball. I gave them my full attention, in hopes that they would ask me if I would like to join them. Then, reality sat in. Animals like me should have a leash on their neck and a muzzle buckled to their mouths. I wouldn't have felt so alienated if my big brother Chris were still here. He had been arrested and sentenced to live in a mental institution for murdering a neighbor's pitbull who got free from its yard.

At the time, Chris and I had no idea that the dog was following us until it began barking at a cat that was trying to get down from a tree. The commotion got our attention, and we stopped to turn around. We had seen that dog plenty of times, wandering the street around the time we headed home from school. The dog darted towards me with its tail wagging. Was the dog approaching me because it could smell the crackers I had in my bookbag, hoping I wouldn't mind sharing them with a hungry dog? Or was the dog in search of a human to play with? Chris and I had no idea. When the dog reached a distance of about a block away from us, its tail was still wagging. I thought this meant it was friendly. Chris had the complete opposite thought.

"Mom! You really think that I'm going to allow you to beat my sister again?!"

Was Chris having a PTSD episode?

I was reminded of the day we first moved into St. Joseph's House For Boys, when Chris made demands of our new foster brothers. He made it clear to them that I had just come from an abusive household, an apartment in East Falls Projects.

There, it was discovered that I was gay. This tarnished the good name of our mom, who was a pastor. In our community, she was suddenly seen as a pastor who accepted the abomination of a gay child. This wasn't true at all. She was a pastor and mother who felt that her son being a girl at heart was just a phase that would soon outlive itself.

Soon after the discovery, a day didn't go by that Mom's church wasn't abandoned. The congregation and the choir, who were once devoted to Mom, joined new churches. They took the story of Mom's humiliation with them to tarnish her reputation even further.

This did not sit well with Mom. She started thinking that if she could break the so-called 'curse' of me being gay, then in return God would give her life back. Mom's eyes left the page of the Bible and went to a book of witchcraft. She searched for the right ways to torture the human body to break curses.

Mom brought her new purpose in life to Chris's attention. At the time, Chris took what she presented to him as a joke. He thought Mom was too invested in honoring the Lord for her to go down such a dark path. He thought Mom was trying to test Chris's belief in her.

Little did Chris know that his little brother was being physically, brutally tortured in so many ways at the hands of his mother. Her methods were inspired by witchcraft.

Chris later explained to me that he could remember, clear as day, the numerous times when I brought freshly-opened bruises to his attention--bruises that he paid no heed to.

Like any dedicated gamer would do, he just pushed me to the side. If only he had pulled me in, offered me alcohol pads and bandages. If only he had been eager to calm the devastating pain my bruises were giving me.

It was three weeks before Mom got arrested. That was when I was finally able to convince Chris to take me seriously. That same day, when he was cornered by a friend he grew up with, who humiliated him in front of the popular boys in the project. He said that there was no way Chris wasn't gay also. This rumor happened to get to Chris's girlfriend. She decided to dump him, rather than endure the embarrassment.

How enraged was Chris? He was like a gorilla running up those project steps, pushing down whoever was in his way. When Chris came into the house, he charged me like a raging bull, sending me flying over the coffee table. Chris got on top of me, brutally punching me in the head and face. It felt as though he wanted to knock some sense into me, convince me to want to be the boy at heart he felt I should be. Both of my eyes swelled shut. My mouth was filled with blood. I wanted to die, but not before I told Chris how I truly felt about him.

"Chris, before I die, I want to say I love you. I hope, one day, you will forgive me for not being the brother you always wanted. I know you were so happy when you found out that Mom was having a boy. My coming-out was a disappointment to the whole family. I was never able to be that momma's boy for Mom, that fishing buddy for Dad. I could never be that brother who you could be proud to play your games with."

Suddenly, the mighty blows to my face and head stopped. I could feel what I thought was warm water dripping down my face. It felt like my upper eyelids had been cut with something sharp. Blood pouring out of my eyelids and onto the floor.

I could see again. My brother was over top of me, crying. That's what I was feeling: Chris's warm tears dripping all over my face, along with his snot. Chris sat me up to have a conversation with me.

"How could you still love me, after I almost beat you to death?! I almost murdered my baby brother! My own flesh and blood! How could I live with myself, knowing I had killed you?!" Chris cried while he rocked me in his arms.

"I forgive you," I said calmly.

"Why? I do not deserve to be forgiven," Chris said despairingly while lifting me up in his arms and laying my helpless body on the sofa. Chris got to his knees by the sofa to hear my reply.

"I bet you were so happy to know that Mom was pregnant with a boy. You thought you would have a brother who you could wrestle and ride big wheeler bikes with. You thought you'd stay up and play with me all night. You'd patiently watch me play your game, only to hear me say at the end that I didn't think anyone could play better than you," I said peacefully.

While rubbing my forehead, Chris said, "I was happy to hear that Mom was having another son. Everything you said was what was going on in my head at the time." Chris headed to the bathroom to get a wet rag, cotton balls, alcohol pads, and bandaids. He brought them back, wrapped in a towel. After lifting the coffee table back on its legs, Chris dumped the first aid items out of the towel and onto the coffee table. At last, he was doing what he should have been doing since the day I was born: being by my side.

While Chris did first aid, I figured I might as well tell him more about me. I hoped that he would be open-minded.

"Chris, can I tell you what I was waiting to tell you all this time?" I asked nervously.

"Spill it, little brother," Chris said compassionately, with a smile. I never saw him do that.

"I think God accidentally made a mistake when creating me. I am a girl trapped in a boy's body. You look at me and you see an eleven year-old boy. I see the same thing. If only we could share the same body and feel each other's emotions. Only then could you feel the girl I am at heart. Mom buys me so many boys' toys. I try to be interested in them so I don't seem ungrateful. But I feel no connection with those toys. There are two large trash bags filled with secrets. While I wait here, do you mind going into my closet and opening up the bags?" I could only have faith that, by revealing my secrets to him, he would understand me better. I sat up on the sofa, crossing my fingers, arms, legs, and eyes for good luck.

"Why are you crossing everything that you can, for all the luck in the world? What are you using all this luck for?" Chris said, confused, before leaving to go to my room.

It would take anyone about a minute to do what I asked. Chris was in there for over five minutes. What was taking him so long? Just when my anxiety was about to take over, Chris stepped out of my room with his thumb on his chin, as though he was unsure what to say to me.

Seconds later, Chris said something that I sure didn't expect.

"Wow, you have every boys' toy that our parents ever bought you. This is very strange. What I mean is: I believe you when you say that you are a boy who is a girl at heart."

I was so excited that I got to my feet, ran towards Chris, and leapt into his arms. He must have assumed that I would do such a thing, because he caught me right away. I was too damn big to do such a thing, but that didn't matter.

"Sirbrian is a name we can no longer call you," Chris said. "From now on, I will call you Donna. No matter who is around. How does that sound?" There was joy in Chris's voice and his heart while he carried me over and sat me down on one of the arms of the sofa.

For the first time, I let out happy tears. Forget about feeling embarrassed; I wanted to show Chris that he had just made me the happiest girl in the world. I was a boy with a brother who saw me as his sister.

"That sounds great," I sighed. I finally had someone in life who loved me for who I was: a girl who was born in a boy's body, whose name was now Donna.

Chris continued to call me Donna, even when I moved into St. Joseph's School For Boys. He demanded that all the other boys call me Donna, too. It took Chris giving out a lot of ass whoopin' for our new foster brothers to honor the name that Chris gave me. I was Chris's little sister and no one was going to take that away from me as long as Chris was around.

There was a part of Chris I knew nothing about. I thought, Did Chris suffer from PTSD after the day he witnessed Devon taking control over my body while fighting with Mom in the kitchen, for the last time?

Like I said before, the dog on the street seemed friendly. Its tail was wagging in the breeze. The pitbull grew anxious and hesitant to come onto the pavement. Could it have been because Chris stood in front of me, armed with heroic intentions? Chris's angry facial expression gave the pitbull a reason to bark at him furiously. That bark must have been the trigger for a side of Chris I had never seen.

"Mom, you really think I'm going to allow you to come back into Donna's life to start where you left off?! Huh!?" Chris said, enraged, as he continued to step forward and back repeatedly. I thought this would have scared the dog off.

I couldn't help but stare at the broken beer bottles, scrap metal and rusted nails under parked cars. Which weapon was Chris going to use to murder the innocent dog? Would his weapon of choice be one of the broken beer bottles, useful for viciously stabbing the pitbull in the chest? Would he use a rusted nail to brutally stab the dog in the eyes? The pitbull would be too busy fighting for its life to realize that it was bleeding to death.

Turning around, I stood up for the dog like it was my own flesh and blood.

"Chris, you have the right to hate Mom for all she put your little sister through. Mom is in prison. Behind me is just a pitbull trying to make a friend," I said calmly. "From here, it looks like the dog has an address collar. I am going to turn around and check to see the address." I stepped back nervously. "See? The dog is happy and wagging its tail. Easy Chris, easy Chris, calm down," I began to be worried about my own safety.

"You don't see the pots falling to the ground around you?! Why ain't you picking one up?! Fool, Mom is beating you with the rolling pin! Grab a fucking pot! Devon is right; you are nothing but a weakling! Is Devon asleep or something? Why the fuck ain't he protecting your body?!" Chris said, outraged.

Chris was definitely in a PTSD episode. Without an alter-ego like mine, he had nothing to help him come back to me, back to the here and now. I was not going to give up on Chris. All we had was each other.

Now Chris was lying on the ground, reaching under a rusted old white pick-up truck for a half-filled 40-ounce beer bottle. After retrieving it, Chris immediately got to his feet. He reached over and broke some of the glass off the top of the bottle. He proudly brandished the weapon to defend against what he thought was Mom.

"Donna, please, I don't want to accidently cut my baby sister. Please just get out of the way. The pot that I have in my hand is cast iron, the unbreakable poor man's pot."

"Chris, you slipped into a PTSD episode. We are no longer in the kitchen where you saw Devon have full control of my body, beating Mom to death with pots, pans, china plates and silverware--whatever he could get his hands on to throw or swing at her. We are in our new neighborhood, standing on the pavement. You are holding a broken beer bottle. I am standing in front of you, blocking your way to an innocent, happy pitbull," I said, calm and easy. What happened next caught me off-guard.

Chris turned to me as if he didn't recognize me at all. "You're one of my Mom's congregation?! You're both trying to team up on my sister Donna! That's right, Donna, stay behind me. Y'all fucked with the wrong big brother!" Chris erupted. He rushed forward, swinging the beer bottle shard at me. I had no choice but to swing my bookbag at him with all my might. It slapped him across the side of his head, causing him to lose balance and fall against the pickup truck. He lost grip of the bottle, which swung out of his hand and into the back of the truck. It shattered into pieces. Enraged, Chris started kicking the truck, forming dents on the driver-side door. Chris was in search of a weapon to murder what he thought was Mom and a homophobic churchgoer.

Chris, in his aggravation, was so focused that he didn't notice the four rusty nails that were on the ground next to his feet. I could only pray that his feet wouldn't stumble over them and realize what they were.

My body started to sweat as my heart throbbed, threatening to send me into an anxiety attack. This could only end with my body being exhausted once again. I would be defenseless against Devon, who would once again take control of my body. If Devon was in control, his mission would be to murder my brother.

"Devon, do you hear me? I know you hear me! Just like you know that the angry man that stands before us is my brother, Chris. A man who you know doesn't honor homophobia," I said, getting overwhelmed.

"And you're telling me this because...?" Devon said, confused.

The Boy of Hearts

"Because I'm asking you to spare Chris's life."

"Spare his life?! Oh, should I just allow him to reach down for the rusty nails by his feet?! I should let him place the nail in between the middle and ring finger of his fist? A fist that will be swung at us, probably towards our head?! I should just let him drive the nail into our skull?! What the fuck is your problem?!" Devon cried.

Chris's foot stumbled over the nails, just like Devon and I had anticipated. Chris placed the rusty nail in between his middle and ring finger, just like Devon had predicted.

"Chris is in a PTSD episode! I will not let you murder the only human that loves me as the girl I am at heart!" I said, petrified.

"Sirbrian, we are about to be stabbed by a rusted nail! Chris is insanely hostile! Get the fuck out of the way!" Devon yelled out to me angrily, taking my attention away from protecting us from being stabbed. While dodging Chris's mighty jabs and uppercuts, I knew that if he landed one blow, I would fall helplessly to the ground. There, I would be vulnerable for him to get on top of me and finish me off.

Devon said, "I will tighten up our lungs so we don't receive any air. Once your dumb ass passes out, I'm going to murder Chris. I don't give a fuck who he is or what state of mind he's in." I could feel Devon closing off my air supply.

Chris stumbled, giving me the opportunity to kick him in the chest. I followed that with a punch to the head that took him to the ground. He laid there for a moment to get himself together. This gave me the chance to get to the back of the truck, fall to my knees and head butt the metal bumper. The head butt put me out cold.

In the moments before I lost consciousness, I could only hope that when Chris got to his feet, the sight of me laying on the ground with my head split down to the white meat would trick him into thinking I was dead.

I woke up in a cold hospital. I was laying on a hospital bed with my head wrapped in a bandage. I held my head, hoping to calm my throbbing headache. I smiled at the sight of Mr. Dan sleeping in a chair, covered with his coat. He really cared about his foster children.

Judging by the amount of takeout platters sitting on the table next to him, he had been waiting by my bed for some time. The doctor came in and told me that I had been unconscious for four days. My memory was just as sharp as ever. As I listened to the opera songs through the speakers, I was proud to be alive. But I couldn't take my mind off of that dog. I wondered if it was still alive. Where was Chris? And wherever he was, was it safe to say that his mind was back in the present? Could he remember how to love his baby sister?

I wanted someone to tell me Chris was in the backyard, deep in the little wooded area, watering our secret garden. Chris decided that we should create and nourish this garden together. In this way, he reminded me every day that he loved me just the way I am.

He taught me that we live in one big world built of many smaller worlds; this is why the world will always be a beautiful place. In the garden, we made worlds of different flowers. It was an enchanted place.

A wave of guilt washed over me; by knocking myself unconscious, I'd left an innocent dog behind to fend for itself against Chris. A pitbull like that would never step down from a fight. This thought terrified me. Could Chris also be here after being brutally attacked by a friendly pitbull turned vicious? I wasn't ashamed to cry. My brother, my only friend and my symbol of acceptance, could be fighting for his life in the other room.

I was going to check every hospital bed, expecting the worst and hoping for the best. Of course, my bright idea fell through; Mr. Dan demanded that I tell the doctor I was fine, and I was soon discharged.

Sitting in the passenger seat of Mr. Dan's van, I listened to him lecture me about how ungrateful I was.

"Listen here, Sirbrian!" Mr. Dan said, frustrated.

"I am not Sirbrian. I am Donna!" I said, rudely.

"Excuse me, last time I checked your birth certificate it said Sirbrian Lee Spease!" Mr. Dan said sarcastically.

"I go by Donna. I've told you that so many times over the years. You don't listen. And you wonder why I don't give a fuck about doing your damn chores!" I said, disrespectfully.

"Look, I never said I do not accept you being gay, now, did I? But I will call you the name that you were given, and that is Sirbrian!" Mr. Dan said, stressed out.

"My fucking parents don't deserve for me to honor that name--especially not my Mom! My name was changed by my brother. It is now Donna and always will be Donna. Whoever can't accept that can lick my boy pussy!" I was irritated as I put on my seat belt.

"You ungrateful motherfucker! I gave up being married and having children of my own. I put in overtime so all you boys could have a better life! Who else at the school besides me shows that they give a damn!" Mr. Dan said, aggravated, while pulling out of the hospital driveway.

"No one," I said, ashamed, while looking into the side mirror.

"That's right, no one! I'm all you've got! I'm just a man who wants your hygiene up to par, your chores done, your homework finished and at least straight B's on your report card. Do I make myself clear?" He asked. I didn't dare answer.

"Boy, am I talking to my motherfucking self?! I have no problem taking away your allowance," he said.

"Of course I hear you! It's not like I can choose not to pay attention when you are screaming instead of talking like a civilized person," I said, irked, while covering my ears.

"Oh, you must hate that I'm forcing you to grow up to be better than your parents. Your parents were selfish and would rather alienate you than love you for who you are."

He continued, "So, you think, 'Fuck getting straight B's on my report card'? Oh, you'd rather keep the family tradition going by being a drop-out! Because the apron at Shop 'N' Bag got your name on it? You're going to be so proud of yourself when you become employee of the fucking month for being the fastest bagger," Mr. Dan said with tough love. "Not under my roof!"

"For your information: if you'd sat down and got to know me, you would've found out that I am far from trying to keep up the tradition of living in the projects. Straight B's? When have you ever seen my report card with lower than an A on it?!" I spat at Mr. Dan defensively.

"Why do you always have to get straight A's? What you tryin' to prove?!" questioned Mr. Dan.

"What? Just because I'm gay doesn't mean I can't be smart."

"And?"

"Just because I'm gay doesn't mean I can't become a doctor or a lawyer or even take up a trade like business or cosmetology. I can even open up my own beauty salon," I said confidently. I was going into silent mode. I wasn't going to continue to embarrass myself by arguing with the only man who had been a parent to me.

Fortunately for me, this was a parent who could care less if I pulled out my traveling makeup kit and lipstick. I did this right away; I was a wreck from the top of my nappy rainbow afro to my neck. I blew the dust off the broken comb I found on the dirty van floor and began picking my hair with it. I proceeded to do my makeup. When I felt satisfied with the way I looked, the comb dropped from my hand and onto the floor. The traveling makeup kit and lipstick went back in my pocket.

Feeling rejuvenated only lasted for a moment. I soon became baffled and then terrified over Chris. The last thing I remembered from that night was a pitbull.

Where was my brother? Had he been hospitalized? If so, Mr. Dan would surely have taken me to him, out of respect. I had no choice but to ask Mr. Dan Chris's whereabouts.

"Mr. Dan," I said calmly.

"Yes, Donna?" Mr. Dan said with compassion. I was completely perplexed; I had no idea what to say next.

The Boy of Hearts

"Well, I mean...umm..." I stuttered, fidgety. "Do you, well, I mean..."

"Donna, what's going on? Are you okay? You're tongue tied!" Mr. Dan said peacefully. "Or is it that you didn't expect me to be so open-minded, so fast?"

"I wasn't expecting you to be so open-minded, so fast, I guess," I said, distraught. While twiddling my thumbs, I said, "Anyway, Mr. Dan, where is Chris? Tell me he didn't get murdered by that pitbull," I said with overwhelming anxiety.

"Actually, it was the other way around. Someone looked out the window and saw your brother strangling that pitbull until it died."

It must have been the neighbors who had built up a resentment towards Chris over the years. He was always beating up their sons when they showed homophobia against me. They all held such animosity in their heart for Chris.

"A group of neighbors came together at St. Joseph's House For Boys to give us an ultimatum. They told us that if we wanted to remain a boy's home and not be shut down for housing a boy who is a danger to the welfare of the neighborhood, we had to admit your brother Chris into a mental institution. Dr. Tan and I, being the head house parent and the house therapist, had no choice but to do what the neighbors requested. We had to save St. Joseph's House For Boys from being shut down," Mr Dan said with a heavy heart.

We reached the house parking lot. I got out of the van, feeling ashamed to be alive. If only I hadn't had so much pride in showing the world that it had no choice but to accept me being gay. Putting up the big fight against a world full of homophobia must have tipped the scales for Chris. It must have brought on his PTSD, a disorder he would have for the rest of his life.

What I wouldn't give to have Chris back in my life! By embracing and loving who I was at heart, I had doomed Chris to being kicked out of our home. I got to move on with my life, but he had to stay in a mental institution.

Chapter 7

Devon Takes Control

Being back at St. Joseph's reminded me of what had happened with Mike and Danny. The boys had had way too many nightmares about me and were fearing for their lives. They were certain I'd bring more harm to them. So Mike and Danny brought the problem to Dr. Tan's attention, in hopes of getting me moved out.

I will never forget the winter day that Dr. Tan yelled out to me. I was making a snow angel like the other boys, feeling like a big ass kid at 15 years old.

"Sirbrian! Are you serious?! Huh?! You promised me that you'd have more self control! You are in need of some serious therapy," Dr. Tan said furiously. He waved at me to come over to him at the front door.

I thought my therapy was working for me. I was actually proud of how far I had come. I had come down from three therapy sessions a week to only one. There had to be some misunderstanding.

I got to my feet, outraged. The other boys quickly got the fuck out of my way; common sense told them to. They were all panicked, remembering what had happened when I got angry the last time. Each one could only hope that he had nothing to do with why Dr. Tan was embarrassing me.

Whatever had happened had to be serious for Dr. Tan to escort me to the basement like he did. Once, I heard that he had a private office down there. It was said that whoever is brought to the basement is most likely going to a mental institution after his session. I thought to myself, Why not have the session where we usually do?

Some of the boys came huddling around the basement door, just to be nosey.

"Dr. Tan, fuck it! Don't even waste your time admitting Donna into a mental institution. We can help you send that freak to Hell! Ain't that right, Mike?" Danny said, hands shaking as he held up a shovel.

"That's right, Danny! Dr. Tan, we can help you dig a grave," Mike yelled, brandishing his own shovel. I could tell from their voices that both boys were terrified.

Devon could feel our anxiety throbbing. After looking through one of our eyes, Devon could surely see he was needed. Devon, who I saw as my best friend, was definitely going to be disappointed in me.

I made a promise to myself: I would no longer put another foster brother in harm's way. It didn't matter if he was a homophobe. I would do anything to keep that promise--not just for him, but for myself.

I couldn't afford to go into a meditation state and let Devon slaughter every boy he could see out of one of our eyes. Hell no! I knew all my foster brothers once lived in dangerous housing projects. They probably had no choice but to fight to the death there, just hoping to see another day. Only I knew what Devon was capable of.

He was a brutal, repulsive, resentful spirit that was attached to my soul. He showed no mercy. My being gay and all made him feel that everyone who did any harm to our body was a homophobe. In Devon's mind, a person who is homophobic should feel two times the pain before he murders them. Luckily, I got Devon to come to the decision to never show his full potential. So killing someone had not happened yet.

I could feel Devon banging on my organs like a raging gorilla. He was doing everything in his power to make our body exhausted. Devon made my right hand into a fist. Out of nowhere, he started punching us in the face. The harder I tried to resist, the harder he hit. Mighty blow after mighty blow struck our face, splitting our lip and busting our nose. Without thinking, Dr. Tan pinned both of our hands against the wall. Devon, feeling us being pinned against our will, turned on beast mode.

What was happening to our body? Every muscle was flexing at once. I saw strength in my arms that I had never seen before. I was deathly afraid of my own arms. I could only watch as old Dr. Tan was lifted up onto the wall. This gave Mike and Danny such a fright that they instantly dropped their shovels on the hallway floor and burst out the front door. The surrounding boys were too scared to even move, let alone speak.

Devon threw Dr. Tan down the flight of basement steps. Now Devon was on top of the helpless Dr. Tan with our hands clenched around his throat, trying to squeeze the life out of him.

"Donna! Promise me you will not blame yourself if Devon happens to kill me. Just so you know, I have always loved you as if you were my blood. In my heart and mind, you are my niece. Never forget, and never let someone convince you otherwise," Dr. Tan said. It was obvious that he was gasping for air.

"Devon, let our uncle go! Let him go! Let Uncle Tan go! You just don't want anyone to love me!" I cried. I pleaded with Devon to have mercy.

How could I save this man's life? I had to think hard and fast. Just then, an idea crossed my mind. I thought it wasn't possible, seeing as Devon had more control of our body at the moment. I focused my mind on all the great times that Dr. Tan and I had shared, the times when he broke out of his shell and saw me as like a niece instead of a patient.

How could I ever forget the time he took me fishing on the lake? Boy, that fish that I almost caught was stronger than me! It almost pulled my fragile body into the water. The fish had no idea that I was just as much fighting for my life as it was. I fought just as hard as I laughed with Dr. Tan afterwards.

What about that time that Dr. Tan helped me conquer my first horrifying experience of being hit by a hard ball? I fell into a PTSD episode right there on the ball field, during the second game we played against St. Anthony's Home For Boys. At that time, I swore that only Devon was able to bring me out of a PTSD episode. It turned out I was wrong. Dr. Tan declared that if any foster boys on either team laughed or gossiped about what they had witnessed, he would call their head house parents and tell them to end their allowances. That shut the mouths of all the boys who played that day.

Slowly, I could feel my and Devon's body growing less tense.

"Donna, what the fuck are you doing to us?! What do you see around Dr. Tan's neck, huh?! Yes, a fucking rosary! He's a man of God! He would say anything to get you down in his torture chamber," Devon said, frustrated.

I ignored Devon's words and pushed his feelings down. "Dr. Tan," I said, "you were the one who told me what being gay is all about. What the letters in LGBT meant. You told me about Stonewall and how gay people are proud to have a gay flag. Why would you, a straight man, teach a gay boy like me all of that? You are the definition of acceptance," I hoped my gratitude would show in my voice.

Once I realized that I was regaining more and more control of my body, I kicked myself off of Dr. Tan and onto the floor.

"Donna, can you hear me?" Dr. Tan said faintly.

"Yes I can, Dr. Tan," I replied in utter exhaustion.

"Do you remember the breathing exercise I taught you? The one you can use to rejuvenate your body? I want you to do that. Breathe through your mouth for three seconds," he began. "Hold your breath for three seconds, then exhale. Keep on repeating the breathing exercise until your body feels refreshed," said Dr. Tan. I could tell he was still gasping desperately for air.

I did what I was told. It took until about my third repeat before my body felt restored. It took Dr. Tan quite a while to gain his strength back. I got to my feet and began heading up the steps backwards, anxious and embarrassed of what Devon and I did.

Who was waiting for me at the top of the stairs? Mr. Dan, of course. He knew something was up.

He was probably thinking, Why am I watching one of my foster sons walking backwards up the stairs? He looks guilty. Mr. Dan observed the scene carefully. He looked past me down the steps, where he saw Dr. Tan lying helplessly on the basement floor.

Mr. Dan charged at me like a raging bull, grabbing hold of my shirt and tossing me behind him onto the steps. He rushed to give aid to Dr. Tan, who looked like he was in agony.

"Dr. Tan, I'm here! Can you hear me? Why is it so damn hard for me to pick the sane boys to live here at St. Joseph's House For Boys?! This is the third time that this has happened to you," Mr. Dan said in shame, falling to his knees beside Dr. Tan.

I got to my feet, but was too afraid to head up the rest of the stairs. I felt my body go as still as possible. Then I became jittery, worried that Mr. Dan was going to brutally beat me like he would an intruder breaking into the house.

"Dan, calm yourself! Do you hear?! Donna had nothing to do with me falling," Dr. Tan explained, weakly patting Mr. Dan on the arm.

"There you go again, standing up for these bad ass boys! I tell you, you can take the boy out of the ghetto but you can't take the ghetto out of the boy!" cried Mr. Dan.

He turned to me. "Boy! If you move, so help me God I will beat you like you stole something," Mr. Dan threatened, giving me the angry eye.

"Mr. Dan Freeman!" Who are you to these boys? Who are you to these boys?!" Dr. Tan said, disturbed by Mr. Dan's repulsive language.

The Boy of Hearts

"I am their head house parent, Dr. Tan," Mr. Dan said sadly. I could hear in his voice that he regretted what he had said to me.

"All these years I've known you, I heard you constantly telling the other house parents to be open-minded. Understand and remember this, Dan! Don't forget where these boys once lived," preached Dr. Tan solemnly.

"I know where these boys came from and the lives they once lived before coming to St. Joseph's," replied Mr. Dan rudely. Dr. Tan shoved Mr. Dan's hand away before getting to his feet.

"And you wonder why I'm here?" Dr. Tan said, leaning against the basement wall.

"To be the house therapist," Mr. Dan said with sarcasm.

"No! To balance this household. You need a therapist to help you raise the boys who came from poverty. What is poverty, Mr. Dan? Please tell us! What is life like in poverty? I want to know," Dr. Tan said.

He turned his face to me and asked. "Do you want to know, Donna? Of course you do," he said with disgust in his voice. While he said this, he pulled me up to stand and took a spot by my side. I no longer felt terrified, as long as I stood by Dr. Tan.

Mr. Dan got to his feet. All I could think was, Are Dr. Tan and Mr. Dan going to physically fight? I sure was about to find out.

"What is life like in poverty," Mr. Dan mused, "where people depend on welfare to get by? Poverty is a place where a mother has no choice but to sell her four hundred dollars in food stamps to a corner store for one hundred and fifty dollars cash in order to buy her children some clothes from the thrift shop. The family has to pray on their way there. They pray to God and ask Him to touch the hearts of the suburban parents and inspire them not to pass their children's outgrown clothing down to relatives as hand-me-downs, donating them instead to the neighborhood thrift store. Why not use the one hundred and ten dollars they are granted by welfare once a month to buy the children used clothes from the thrift shop? Because that money, along with the money that they received from the Emergency Utility Assistance Program, all goes to paying their bills.

"So why would that mother rather have her children starve than go without winter clothes? When it comes down to feeding her children, she has that covered. She's there bright and early at the food banks and bakeries to accept food that would be outdated in a day or two. She accepts the food that was rejected by society, like produce that is cast out only because it is disfigured. She thinks, There will never come a day when my child will starve. There is always going to be a dumpster with her name on it.

The Boy of Hearts

"She is willing to sit in this dumpster all day if she has to, in order to retrieve the bag filled to the top with food that once sat on the rack of the local fast food spot. The nighttime closer at the restaurant may have thought they were throwing the bag into the dumpster for the trashman to dispose of. But they really have no idea that the trash bags that are thrown in the dumpster fall into the arms of a mother who is grateful to have food to take home to her children," Mr. Dan finished gloomily.

"Mr. Dan, would you like to continue this story in my office? Because this man," Dr. Tan said, pointing to himself, "ain't young like he used to be. There was a time when I was able to stand for hours, but right now, I'm exhausted."

Did Mr. Dan have a secret of his own? Mr. Dan looked back and forth from me to Dr. Tan. His face looked flustered and unhappy.

Instead of answering Dr. Tan (which would have been the respectful thing to do), Mr. Dan stood in front of me and pulled me to his chest to embrace me in the kind of hug that he had never given me before. I imagined that this was Mr. Dan's way of saying sorry because he was too ashamed to say it out loud. Mr. Dan made his way silently up the stairs and out the door, shutting it behind him.

I turned to Dr. Tan, a gentleman and a man I loved like an uncle. I helped him into his office, lending him my shoulder to lean on for balance until we got there.

Dr. Tan sat down in his chair and pulled himself up to his desk while I surveyed the room. What I saw left me just as confused as I was startled and displeased. When I arrived at St. Joseph's House For Boys, I was promised by The Department of Human Services that here I would be relieved from child abuse. What I saw in front of me made me doubt that.

Chapter 8

A Girl at Heart

The office had three white walls. The wall behind Dr. Tan was filled with three by five pictures of him with boys of different races and ages. The small wall that was connected to the door we came through had scratch marks so deep that you could see the sheet rock. The wall to my right had straight jackets and belts hanging on the wall from floor to ceiling. At eye level on the same wall was a wooden shelf where worn-out, padded helmets sat. On my left, where a fourth wall was supposed to be, was a plexiglass barrier attached to a padded door. Through the plexiglass, I could see that the walls, ceiling, floor and door were covered in white padding.

Was this another torture chamber? Did Dr. Tan become a therapist to hide his secret sadist identity?

The Boy of Hearts

With these doors closed, was he going to reveal that he was a pastor? And not just your ordinary pastor, a pastor who knew my mom? Was he willing to show my mom how much he honored their friendship by picking up where she had left off with her son? Would he pull out Mom's witchcraft book from some secret compartment? Would it be open to Chapter Eight-- "On How to Use Spells and Torture Devices to Break Curses"--before I could blink? I got to my feet and reached back to open the door as wide as it could go before sitting back down. I discreetly dragged my chair closer to the open door. If anything out of the ordinary happened, I would have a way to escape.

"Donna, I know that all of our previous sessions have been upstairs at the kitchen table. The noises of the house around us remind me not to go over the time limit. But when I feel like a boy needs intensive therapy, I prefer to do it down here where we are isolated from interruptions. Does that make sense?" Dr. Tan explained.

"I guess so," I said in confusion, while my anxiety grew. I kept my eyes on Dr. Tan's hands.

"Now, if I was in your shoes, the sight of the straight jackets and restraint belts and padded helmets would creep me out. It would be strange for me to be in a room with a padded cell. If you look up, you will see a TV on a metal beam. This beam helps the TV adjust to come down in front of the plexiglass barrier. Some therapy that I do down here requires a TV," Dr. Tan said calmly.

"Before we start our session, were you planning on putting me in a straight jacket and escorting me into the padded cell?" I asked. "Look, are you a pastor? Were you sent into my life to finish the job my Mom started?! Doctor, Sir, you are wasting your time and you are about to put your life in danger. You have no idea what I'm capable of," I said in outrage, while leaning forward and pushing down on the top of Dr. Tan's desk. I thought my outburst would have startled him, but it didn't. Dr. Tan held his composure, like a true professional.

He cleared his throat and said, "I wasn't sent by your mother to pick up where she left off. But after what you have been through, I'm not surprised you think that. You were attacked for your first love, Prince, who you fell in love with at the age of five. You were also born a boy but are a girl at heart. Am I right so far, Donna?" His expression changed. "Is your body growing weak? Is Devon trying to take over your body? Am I in danger? Can I continue?" I could hear the fear in his voice as he spoke.

"You are right so far," I replied. "You are safe. Continue."

"Now, when you took Prince into your imaginary world, your body was transformed from a boy into a princess. In your imaginary world, you danced at a ball with Prince in front of all the other royalty. You didn't want to go back to reality because there, you were a boy who happened to be a girl at heart. You destroyed your mother's good name. She was no longer seen as a respected pastor, because how could a pastor have a gay child?" Dr. Tan paused, then asked, "Am I still okay?"

"I still have control of my body, Dr. Tan. Continue."

"The daily walk of shame through the neighborhood drove your mother mad. She became so insane that she went from being a pastor, honoring God, to being a witch, honoring witchcraft. She learned what she thought were spells and ways to torture your body that would set demons free. She believed that you had been possessed by demons and it was her responsibility to get them out. The witchcraft book had hundreds of ways to torture the human body. Trust and believe, she was ready to try all of them to find the right one that would break the so-called 'curse' of you being gay. Am I good to continue?" Dr. Tan said, nearly overwhelmed with the fear of Devon coming out.

"Dr. Tan, I told you that I was fine. Stop panicking!" I said, irritated.

"Okay, Donna. So, you were being abused. Scar after scar covered your body. It got so bad that you never went swimming at the public pool because you were so self-conscious. You worried that, from a distance, strangers would've sworn that your body was covered in blood-sucking leeches," Dr. Tan said, fear still present in his voice.

"Wow! You remembered all that I told you during those two days when we had sessions at DHS, when I lived at their transition center before I was placed at St. Joseph's House for Boys!" I was astonished at how great Dr. Tan's memory was.

"The first day we met, I told you: I will do all I can to help you cope with your PTSD. Look how far you've come! You have mastered every method I've taught you, from meditation to visualization to bringing yourself into the now. There's not one grounding skill you don't know! Have there been times you were at war with Devon over control of your body and won?"

"Yes, there have!" I said, genuinely proud of myself.

"There will be days when you're not strong enough to win against Devon, but that's okay. It doesn't matter how much you try to avoid getting yourself into those situations. And why is that, Donna?" said Dr. Tan.

"Because no one is perfect," I replied.

"Bingo! I've noticed that you're no longer letting name calling bother you. Why is that?" questioned Dr. Tan.

"Because people can say all they want about me. At the end of the day, all that matters is how I react." The fear that Dr. Tan had brought me down here to finish what Mom had started was no longer on my mind or in my heart. But I knew I had to be down here for some reason.

"Donna, do you trust me? Do you believe that I will never hurt you?" questioned Dr. Tan compassionately. He leaned down and started rubbing my shoulder.

"Yes. I have to learn how to believe that not everyone in the world holds homophobia in their hearts. Some people believe that the Bible is just a book of stories that a human being created to make others into believers of God. Maybe that writer was a homophobic person who wanted to brainwash the world and alienate the gay community. Who knows? What matters is that I believe I am safe in your hands, Dr. Tan," I said with conviction.

"I would like to have a private conversation with Devon. Could you make that happen?" Dr. Tan asked me cautiously.

"Of course I can, Dr. Tan! But I must warn you: Devon could go from aggravated to enraged, and from enraged to furious, in no time," I said with concern for Dr. Tan's safety.

"I remember you telling me that during our first therapy session. This is why I decided to have our therapy session here in my office. It's for my own safety. Can you allow me to put you in a straight jacket before escorting you into the padded cell? Then I will feel safe allowing Devon to take full control of your body," Dr. Tan said with perfect calm while gesturing to the straight jackets on the wall and the padded cell to the side of the room.

I thought to myself, Why not allow him to restrain me? I was concerned about Dr. Tan, so I showed him no resistance.

There I was, looking through the plexiglass at Dr. Tan while strapped into a straight jacket, seated on the padded floor. Dr. Tan decided to roll his chair in front of the plexiglass before sitting down. He waited patiently while I began to meditate.

I journeyed through my thoughts until I reached the most terrifying and devastating scene, the one that no person should ever witness. Witnessing it would put anyone into my poor brother Chris's shoes.

I was back in the projects, sitting in Mom's torture chair. It was painted in rainbow colors to represent the gay flag. Of course, Mom didn't create such a chair off the top of her head. Always the copycat, she created the contraption using instructions found in an old, raggedy, damp, witchcraft book.

I sat there in my own shit and pee, body fully nude with fresh bruises and deep cuts scattered all over my body. My head, neck, shoulders, arms, waist, legs, and feet were strapped to the chair by belts that were also painted like each stripe of the rainbow flag.

The Boy of Hearts

I saw Mom come in, pulling a hand truck of
different colors of paint. My body grew weak, knowing
what was coming next.

Devon awoke.

"What the fuck is happening?! Where are we?!
Why did you wait until we were strapped to a fucking
chair to awake me, fool?!" Devon screamed, petrified.
He assumed that Mom was back in our life, back to
repeat some of the worst torture she had ever done.
Devon was so busy jumping to conclusions that he
didn't stop to think that I could be meditating to give
the body over to him on purpose.

"Did you forget we share our thoughts?" I
asked him, annoyed. "Can you see our hands, arms,
and legs?"

"No I can't, Donna," Devon said. "Oh, I guess
you're right. It's my fault for disrespecting you. I can
feel you losing strength and me gaining strength. Let
me see what's going on." I could tell that Devon was
puzzled. He looked out of our right eye, where he saw
what he thought was the inside of a mental institution.
But that wasn't the case at all.

While I was trapped in a nightmare with Devon in
full control of the body, I respected Dr. Tan's wishes. I
didn't sneak a peek out of one eye or focus on hearing
what Dr. Tan and Devon were discussing. I assumed that
I probably didn't have the strength to do it anyway.

There was Mom again, splashing me with different colors of paint.

"So you want to be a damn rainbow? Huh?! Answer me, you fucking faggot! A rainbow even at fucking night?! You will hate rainbows when I'm done with you!" she cried. "It burns, doesn't it? So cry! You're not crying hard enough! Cry out the abomination that you refuse to release from your soul!" Mom's anger was overwhelming.

I cried out in agonizing, miserable pain. The acid from the paint was eating at the white meat in between my fresh bruises. I could feel my heart throbbing. Was it going to burst? I yearned for Dr. Tan to end his therapy session. But it wasn't until an hour had passed that I could feel my body growing exhausted.

Devon broke his silence and said to me, "Donna, Dr. Tan told me that he has some amazing socialization therapy method that he has in store for you. Dr. Tan told me to step to the side and give his therapy time to work. After listening to Dr. Tan explain all the component methods that create socialization therapy, I became a believer. I believe that socialization therapy will replace me. You won't need me to protect you any longer. But understand that I will always be here in the background, so you will never be alone!"

Devon was exhausted as we exchanged control of the body for the last time. Soon, I was in full control again and I understood that I would be for a long time.

The Boy of Hearts

Will I miss Devon just a little? Maybe. I can only pray that this socialization therapy can take me to a place I have never been. I would love to be inside a circle of people who love me for me. I left the padded cell, stood at the top of the basement stairs and whispered, "I know that the day will come when someone will love me as the girl I am at heart."

The End

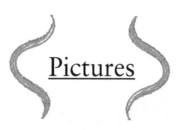

Pictures

Me on the swing on the property of St. Joseph's House For Boys, talking to Prince on the swing next to me. We talked about all the good times we had in the bathroom at the East Falls Project apartment that I once lived in with my family. The world would say there was no one there on the swing next to me, but you couldn't convince me of that.

Me when I went to Wordsworth Academy, a mental health school.

A time when Devon had our body. He was standing up to my foster brothers, like he always did. He was ready to do bodily harm. I sure wasn't proud of being a part of those moments.

Me at the House for Boys writing a letter to my alter-ego, Devon. I told him, in so many words, to take it easy on our foster brothers.

My overprotective brother, Chris, at St. Joseph's House for Boys with me. I was so heartbroken when he was taken away from me and put in a child mental institution, leaving me alone. If he had never killed that dog, we would've grown up together.

Me at sixteen years old with my secret family: the ducks. I could count on them to accept me for who I was. I think about those ducks sometimes.

A.B.O. is a collective of creators and activists who work to amplify the voices of LGBTQ prisoners through art. By working closely with prison abolitionist and queer advocacy organizations, we aim to keep queer prisoners connected to outside community and help them in the fight toward liberation. The profits we generate go back to incarcerated artists, especially those with little to no resources. Using the DIY ideology of "punk-zine" culture, A.B.O. was formed with the philosophy of mutual support, community and friendship.

Our collective is working towards compassionate accountability without relying on the state or its sycophants. A.B.O. believes our interpersonal and societal issues can be solved without locking people in cages. Our mission is to combat the culture that treats humans as disposable and disproportionatly criminalizes the most marginalized amongst us. Through artistic activism, we hope to proliferate the idea that a better world means redefining our concepts of justice.